KU-314-427

© Alberto Peruzzo Editore and Studio Creazioni Dami.

UNUSUAL FEEDERS
OF THE
ANIMAL WORLD

TEXT CONTRIBUTED BY

MAURICE BURTON, D.Sc.

ODHAMS BOOKS LIMITED

LONG ACRE, LONDON

INTRODUCTION

Food is essential to life. It provides the fuel that drives the living engine. While the principles governing the way animals feed are fairly uniform throughout the million or more different kinds of animals living today, each of these species has at least one peculiarity. This may be in the kind of food it takes or in the way it deals with it. There are also individual idiosyncrasies within each species. It follows therefore that the subject of food and feeding methods cannot be dealt with fully in a book of this size. Nor is this desirable since so often a background of technical knowledge is needed to understand what is taking place. Consequently, this volume deals only with a few selected examples of some of the more peculiar ways in which animals feed, what they eat and the effect the food has on them.

We can divide people into vegetarians and meat-eaters, but no such simple classification is possible with animals. Some animal vegetarians are called herbivores and these include the browsers that eat leaves and twigs and grazers that eat grass. Other animal vegetarians are leaf-eaters or fruit-eaters. Animal meat-eaters may be carnivores, that is, flesh-eaters, or insect-eaters, and there are fish-eaters and many others. There are also many animals that are scavengers, feeding on dead flesh or dead plants. There are particulate feeders, those that strain tiny particles or bacteria, or both, from water or mud. And there are even animals that take food in through the skin. The tapeworm in an animal's stomach imbibes liquid food, so that it deprives its host of nourishment. Such an animal has no mouth and usually no digestive canal. There are also animals that, while feeding through the skin, do not parasitize others but live in water, drawing their nourishment from substances in solution in the water. Finally, there are omnivores, animals that will eat almost anything edible. Rats are a good example, and pigs run them a close second.

There are some people whose tastes are so catholic and their appetites so hearty that we say of them, jokingly, that they will eat everything except broken bottles. There is one animal that will do even this, the North American porcupine.

GLASS BOTTLES NOT REFUSED

The **North American porcupine,** usually called the Canada or Canadian porcupine, varies its food with the seasons. In spring it eats the flowers and catkins of the willow, maple and poplar. Later it turns to the new leaves of aspen and larch. Being a tree climber it can reach these. In summer it feeds more on herbaceous plants and in winter on evergreens like the hemlock and pine. But its principal food in winter is bark, and porcupines do much damage by ring-barking trees. This, however, is not the end. It has a strong liking for sweet corn and a few porcupines can leave a field of it ravaged.

This porcupine has another vice: a craving for salt. Handles of farm implements where hands moistened with sweat have touched them, leaving a trace of salt, will be gnawed. So will gloves, boots, saddles, and even the steering wheel of a car has been gnawed away. The porcupine will gnaw bones as well as antlers dropped by deer. But its crowning achievement is to gnaw glass bottles thrown away by campers, presumably for the salt in the glass. Even so, the porcupine is not an omnivore: it is a vegetarian with additional tastes.

There is a division of opinion about how much destruction the North American porcupine causes among trees. Some writers maintain that while it often damages the bark of trees and may kill valuable timber and ornamental trees, this kind of destruction is usually insignificant. It is difficult to reconcile the two parts of this statement. What is probably meant is that the damage tends to be localized and sporadic. For example, this porcupine occasionally destroys the young red fir of the Sierra Nevada in California. This happens when the snow lies deep and the porcupine is forced to live in the same tree for an appreciable length of time. It may then strip all the bark above the snow-line, so killing the tree.

GOOD FOOD MAKES BIG BEARS

For an example of an omnivore we cannot do better than study the brown bear. It is also a very good example of how the diet not only influences behaviour but also influences the appearance of the animal, in both its size and the colour of its coat.

Brown bears used to be found throughout Europe and most of Asia as well as North America. Usually they are divided into many species, of which the best known are the European brown bear and the North American grizzly bear. The difference between these two is largely a matter of size, the grizzly bear often reaching 880 lbs. weight and a length of 8½ feet, whereas the European bear, certainly at the present time, averages 6 feet in length and a weight of 500 lbs. The grizzly is not the largest brown bear, however, because the Kenai bear and the Kodiak bear, both of Alaska, reach a weight of 1,650 lbs. and a length of 9 feet or more.

Some scientists take the view that all the brown bears of the northern hemisphere consti-

North American porcupine *(Erethizon dorsatum)*

tute a single species and that the differences between them are the result of living in different places and, more especially, feeding on different food. One reason for taking this view is that there have been found in museums in Russia skins of bears as large as some of the largest North American brown bears, even as large as the Kenai and Kodiak bears. Conversely, we know that even grizzly bears differ in size and weight from one place to another and some of them are no bigger than an average European brown bear. These differences are almost certainly the result of differences in food. On the other hand, it seems fairly certain that differences in the colour of the coat of the various grizzly bears, which may vary from light yellowish grey to a bluish black, are influenced by the climate.

A brown bear's diet sheet may include insects of many kinds, honey, many kinds of plant food including roots, tubers and berries, small mammals such as mice and squirrels, deer fawns, porcupines or even large cattle on occasion. Carrion also is eaten. The largest bears, those on Kodiak Island and on the Kenai peninsula, in Alaska, when they come out of their winter quarters, feed abundantly on the carcases of sea birds, whales, seals and walruses as well as dead fish lying along the shore. They also feed on the large quantities of seaweed cast up on the shore. Later in the spring they gorge themselves on the fresh green grass and other plants that spring up as the snows melt. In summer the streams are filled with salmon running up the rivers to spawn and in autumn the spent salmon, those that have spawned and are dead and dying, come down the rivers. The bears flip the salmon out onto the bank with their paws or wade into the water and actually seize them. In autumn also there is a wide variety of berries of all kinds and by the time winter arrives these huge bears go back into their winter quarters fat and well-fed.

This is true only of the **Kenai bears** living on or near the coast. Further inland where there is not such abundant food their fellows seldom reach 1,000 lbs. weight as compared with the 1,650 lbs. of the coast-dwelling Kenai bears.

The bears living near the salmon rivers seem to know when the fish can be expected and assemble along the banks of the rivers, especially near the falls. At all times they live solitary lives, even when they congregate along the river banks they are still solitary animals. Each keeps its distance from its neighbours, taking up a certain strip of river bank and occupying it as a territory. If another bear wanders into this territory there will be a show of aggression on the part of the occupant. If the newcomer is the smaller of the two it will retreat. If it is larger, the owner of the territory will give up possession but if the two are evenly matched there is likely to be a vicious fight.

This same kind of behaviour is largely responsible for the stories of bears attacking human beings. As a rule they shun human beings, but if a bear comes across a camp site or a hut where there are stores of food and the owners of it are away it adopts this as its territory just as it would a piece of the river bank when a salmon run is on. Then when the human owner returns he becomes, in the eyes of the bear, an intruder into its territory and the bear attacks as it would have if another bear were intruding.

The other times when the bears are dangerous are when the she-bears have their cubs with them. To get between the cubs and the mother bear is asking for trouble, but this is not because the bear harbours malicious intentions towards human beings as such. For the explanation we have to go back to the banks of the salmon rivers. The she-bear comes down to get the salmon, just as the male bear does. She leaves her cubs at a safe distance from the bank and goes to the water's edge to fish, but all the time she has one eye on the cubs because a large male bear is as likely to kill a cub and eat it as to go and fish. Therefore, if another bear goes anywhere near her cubs the mother bear immediately turns from the river and charges, and the bears themselves know that there is no more formidable opponent than a she-bear defending her cubs, so they rapidly retire. Similarly, a human being going anywhere near the cubs will be treated the same as a large bear would be treated and the mother will attack with fury.

Even a tame bear, acting without malice, can inflict damage because of its powerful arms and stout claws. So an infuriated bear is best given a wide berth. It is almost certainly the behaviour of the she-bear with her cubs that has given the brown bears their bad reputation, which has resulted in their persecution throughout the centuries, both in Europe and in North America.

Kenai bear (*Ursus kenaiensis*) ➡

BEARS CHEW DYNAMITE

The unusual foods that some animals eat can have very serious or at least awkward consequences for humans. One example of this occurred in Canada, in the Rocky Mountains, an area where avalanches are very prevalent at the time of the melting snows. The Canadian authorities had on hand an anti-avalanche scheme, whereby when the snow on a mountain side seemed likely to be in danger of slipping and causing an avalanche, it was blasted away with dynamite before it could cause any damage.

In theory this appeared a most excellent and practical scheme, and has indeed had successful results elsewhere. But unfortunately for the Canadians, they had to abandon their plans, and seek some other way of preventing avalanches. They had, it seems, overlooked the arch-omnivore. The **grizzly bears** which abound in that area developed a taste for dynamite, and ate the sticks of explosive, thereby successfully baulking any attempt to prevent the avalanches.

HYAENAS AS PREDATORS

Extensive studies have been made in East Africa recently of **spotted hyaenas** as a result of which the conventional picture of these well-known animals is completely changed. Hyaenas have always been thought of as scavenging the remains of game dead from natural causes or killed by other animals, especially by lions. Now a closer and more detailed observation of them has been made whereby our opinions need radical alteration.

For years past hyaenas have often been seen making a meal by day off the remains of a Thomson's gazelle left by a lion. In addition, it has been a common sight for travellers in Africa to see vultures coming down from the skies onto the remains of a kill, and in so doing attracting hyaenas to the spot. These things have been seen so often that the idea became accepted that hyaenas were almost entirely scavengers. Now, for the first time, they have been observed at night, by a Dutch scientist who followed them in a land rover. As a result we have a much more complete picture of their methods of feeding.

During the day hyaenas normally sleep in holes, under rocks or in the shade of trees. At dusk they wander around meeting other hyaenas and thus form the hyaena "pack". Together they walk off in a fixed direction, sometimes keeping close together and at other times

Grizzly bear (*Ursus horribilis*)

spreading out. They may cover miles in this way until the quarry is spotted — zebra and wildebeest are the most usual. If the prey is zebra the hyaenas, with heads down, walk right up to the group of them. Zebras live in family parties of a stallion and several mares and their young. At the approach of the hyaenas, the stallion turns to defend while the rest of his family runs, but not very fast, sometimes even stopping, to look round. The point is that with their stallion in the rear they have no leader to take them away quickly.

The hyaenas then form a crescent, almost as if acting in concert, but they are still hunting as individuals and each pursues the group of zebras biting at the legs or soft parts of one of them whenever the opportunity occurs. In due course, one adult zebra, perhaps, may be hampered in her movements by one of the hyaenas and falls back from the rest. Immediately all the other hyaenas will concentrate on this one animal and finally bring it to the ground. Now, they really are acting in concert and the zebra is helpless. Death is swift and in about half an hour the hyaenas will have devoured every scrap of the prey, including the bones. A characteristic of hyaenas is their enormously powerful jaws and teeth with which they can masticate even the long bones.

The hunt for wildebeeste is slightly different from that of zebra. The hyaenas charge in among a large herd and as soon as one hyaena has a firm grip on one of the wildebeeste all the other hyaenas converge on the victim. The wildebeeste is far swifter in running than a zebra as well as being prone to turn and attack, with its horns. One of its peculiarities is that often while being chased it will run into water and when it does this it is caught almost immediately by the hyaenas.

Hyaenas are by no means always successful in their hunting. In the case of zebra this may be because some groups run away faster than others and with prolonged running could certainly outpace hyaenas, who would soon tire at any great speed. Hyaenas appear, however, to be more strongly attracted to zebra than to wildebeeste since they will roam for many miles to get near zebra when there are large herds of wildebeeste all around them.

Night hunting does not, of course, rule out scavenging. In fact, where packs of hyaena live near a village they often invade it and clear up anything edible left lying around. Also during the day they are more likely to eat other animals' kills or to kill small animals. There is no doubt that it was these habits that caused the characteristic of "meanness" to be attributed to hyaenas as a whole.

Usually hyaenas do not move around at random, but stay more or less within the same range. The separate groups, each numbering from 10 to 100, living on the same range, have now become known as "clans". The females seem to adhere quite strictly to the clan-range whereas the males are more given to wander.

Clan-ranges are also territories in the usual sense and as such are defended by the resident clan. It may happen that after a long chase, a kill is made within the range of another clan. A struggle may then ensue, between the rival hyaenas, with threatening postures and chasing, but only rarely does a real fight develop. The outcome of a "clan-struggle" over a carcase is determined by the position of the kill in relation to the territorial "boundary". The hyaenas in occupation of the territory in which the kill lies are the more likely to win, because they are on their home ground. But if the invaders are more hungry than the occupying clan they may win.

In some places the main prey of the hyaena migrate through vast areas and the hyaenas follow, but there have also been found permanent clan territories from which the resident hyaenas make excursions of several days duration to where the game is, often more than 50 miles away.

Spotted hyaena *(Crocuta crocuta)*

Pheasant (*Phasianus colchicus*)

A CROP FULL OF INSECTS

The **pheasant** is a native of Asia that has been introduced to countries far distant from its original home. In Britain the bird is commonly seen in the countryside, and the more obvious signs of its feeding can be seen in fields of root-crops, such as turnips. But if there is one bird more than another that deserves the name of omnivore it is the pheasant. As one writer has said, it is easier to list the things it does not eat. It will not only peck pieces out of turnips but almost any kind of green leaf, seed, tuber or fleshy root, berries or fruit of almost any kind, ferns and toadstools, insects, earthworms, slugs, snails, lizards and small snakes, and even small rodents and small birds have been found in the crops of pheasants. If we judge from the pheasant with eight baby adders, Britain's only poisonous snake, in its crop the answer to those who ask how to rid their land of adders should be to keep pheasants. On several occasions pheasants have been shot in fields where grain was being grown, on the assumption that the birds were eating grain. The crop of one of these was found to contain no grain, but was filled with 1,670 wireworms, the most noxious of insect larvae to the farmer. Another contained $2\frac{1}{2}$ ounces of the larvae of the St. Mark's fly, another troublesome insect.

BEE IN THE HOLE IS TOAD'S DINNER

Toads may not have the varied diet seen in pheasants, simply because they take no plant food. At the same time they excel not only in the diversity of their food but even more in the astonishing amount of food they will take, as if they had no sense of repletion. One **European common toad** was seen to swallow so many earthworms in succession that in the end it passed the worms alive. A nineteenth-century writer said of the common toad that its food seemed to consist of all living animals that are susceptible of being swallowed. There is only one condition to be fulfilled: a toad takes only moving prey. It is movement which catches its attention, after which it follows the course of the prey for a few seconds, adjusts its position, then flicks out its tongue to make a capture.

Its diet includes insects and their larvae, especially beetles and ants, as well as woodlice, worms, snails, baby newts, young frogs and also young toads, young slow-worms and newly-hatched grass snakes. The last of these is ironic because one of the main enemies of the adult toad is the adult grass snake. Ants are a particularly favourite food of the common toad, and one toad was found to have 363 ants in its stomach. Some toads are also fond of bees and will sit beside the entrance to a hive in the evening picking off the bees as they return home. The remarkable thing is that under test some toads soon learnt to avoid bees while others continued to take them. It seems that some toads quickly learn how to avoid being stung while others fail to do so, and are stung, thereafter avoiding the bees.

European common toad (*Bufo bufo*)

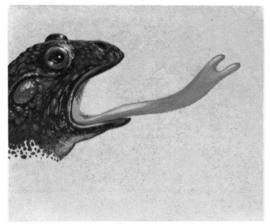

North American bullfrog (*Rana catesbeiana*)
with tongue extended

HOW A FROG'S TONGUE WORKS

The **North American bullfrog** is nearly as bad
as the European common toad in being able to
prey on almost anything not too large for it to
swallow. It also happens to be the species of
amphibian to be most closely studied to find
out how it catches its prey.

For a very long time we have been saying quite
happily that the way frogs and toads feed is by
means of a sticky tongue hinged at the front of
the mouth which can be shot out and withdrawn, the prey going back into the mouth
because it is temporarily stuck to the tongue by
the saliva. With the development of high-speed
photography we now know that the process is
more complicated than this. The tongue is
moistened with saliva, but it is true to say that
any saliva is viscid and therefore more or less
an adhesive.

Dissection of the bullfrog's tongue shows that
there is a pad of muscle at the base of it, which
is seated on two very small bones where the
two halves of the lower jaw meet. As the bullfrog leaps at its prey its mouth is already open
and in the split second as the mouth gets near
the prey this combination of bones and muscle
come into action and catapult the tongue forward, to a length of nearly four inches, in large
frogs and toads. The end of the tongue is
forked and it whips round the body of the prey
as the end of a whip wraps round a post. So
there is a certain amount of grip in the tongue
in addition to the sticky saliva. Furthermore,
the tongue is covered with hundreds of tiny
papillae so that its surface is almost like a file.
These assist the grip because the papillae
become inserted into any irregularity on the

Four stages in a bullfrog's leap for a butterfly. Note
action of the tongue.

13

surface of the prey. Another set of muscles withdraws the tongue, the whole operation taking about a fifteenth of a second. So it is not merely a sticky tongue, it is also a whippy tongue and a rough tongue that enables the frog or the toad to seize its food.

Ten years ago other photographs were taken, using electronic flash, to show the working of the tongue of the North American common toad. In this case, the main feature of the experiment was that the toad was photographed catching mealworms. Each mealworm was held in a light grip by a small spring clamp. The toad had no difficulty in pulling the mealworm with its tongue from the spring clamp that held it, which would not have been possible if stickiness of the tongue had been the only means by which the toad held its prey.

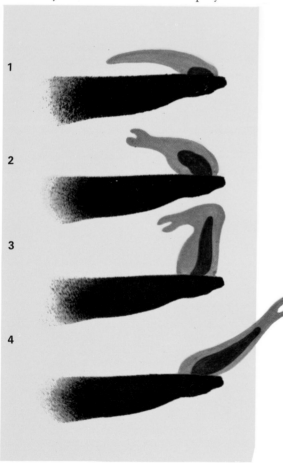

A bullfrog's tongue

1: The tongue at rest, lying in the floor of the mouth.
2-4: Successive stages in throwing out the tongue (the dark area is the tongue muscle).

CUNNING OLD BABOON

If a toad appears to have an over-weaning gluttony it is because it has neither the intelligence nor the capability for storing excess food. Higher in the animal scale, among birds and mammals, the hoarding of excess food is a marked feature of the animals' behaviour. A squirrel burying nuts is a typical example, but more intelligent was the stratagem used by a baboon.

Baboons live in troops and together they go out each day foraging, turning over the stones for insects and scorpions, and picking up any fruit, grain or vegetables they may find. Where in Africa the ground is tilled they do enormous damage to the crops because these provide an easy living. A troop of baboons must always be on the look-out for enemies, so they try to obtain as much food as possible in the shortest time they can. In this they are assisted by their capacious cheek pouches, into which they can stuff food and carry off more than can be eaten on the spot.

A writer in *Scientific American* several years ago told how an old male **chacma baboon** increased the amount he could carry away. This old male lived on his own away from the troop. There were a number of leopards in the district and leopards are particularly fond of baboon. This old male baboon seemed to have been determined not to be caught napping when raiding the maize crops. He would bind a piece of rope or a vine around his middle and when he came to a field of maize or a place where it was stored he would push the cobs under his belt in case he had to leave in a hurry. On one occasion he ambushed two women who were on their way to market with baskets of the grain on their heads. The baboon stepped out on to their path, made terrifying noises and gestures at them so that they panicked and fled leaving the maize scattered on the path. The baboon collected this up and made off with it.

ALMOST WHOLLY VEGETARIAN

So much of the information about the habits of African and other monkeys comes from individuals kept in captivity. We know enough about some of them in the wild to be certain that there are changes in their behaviour when they are confined in cages, and there are also changes in their feeding habits. Unfortunately, all too often the food they take in the wild is either unknown or only partially known, but there is one species of **white-nosed guenon** on

Chacma baboon *(Papio ursinus)*

which we have fairly full details.

We ordinarily think of the food of monkeys as being fruit, leaves, insects, birds' eggs, even small birds and small mammals, and this is how it is often stated in print. Several years ago A. J. Haddow wrote about his very close studies of the white-nosed guenon in the forests of tropical Africa, where it is one of the commonest monkeys. He studied more especially their food. His observation of 500 of these monkeys in the wild state showed that with three exceptions they ate nothing but plant foods. These three ate large quantities of ants of a kind with particularly vicious stings. They would make a meal of anything up to a thousand of these ants and it is difficult to explain why they should do it. It might have been that the ants had some medicinal value. When these animals are kept in captivity they are known to eat insects and even to pull small birds to pieces when they fly into their cages. It looks therefore as if the most confirmed animal vegetarian can turn carnivore readily given the temptation to do so. In this connection it is interesting to find that in Uganda white-nosed guenons have, on two occasions, in widely separated places, been responsible for the wanton slaughter of domestic poultry. In default of other information we can only suppose these were individuals that, dietetically speaking, had gone off the rails. They may have been individuals that had left their troop, or been driven out and were living apart. This not infrequently happens with social animals.

White-nosed guenon *(Cercopithecus nictitans)*

Diana monkey (*Cercopithecus diana*)

STRICT VEGETARIANS, ALL BUT!

The meat-eating habits of the human race are often contrasted with the exclusively vegetarian diets of our nearest relatives, the large apes. While gorillas seem to be wholly vegetarian, and chimpanzees nearly so, it has been shown recently that the latter will on occasion eat the flesh of small game. Whether they kill these themselves is still doubtful. Monkeys, also, will occasionally do so, like the **Diana monkey** in the London Zoo, which was seen stalking in the manner of a cat a sparrow that had entered its cage. Having caught the sparrow it twisted off the bird's head, as if used to the operation, and then ate every part of it, including the bones. Monkeys are not the only animals that, while being predominantly herbivorous, have quite often been observed to turn carnivorous, killing and eating both birds and animals. Certain kinds of deer and antelope in particular do this. **Red deer** in Richmond Park, in England, have been known to take rabbits that have been caught in snares. On one occasion a hind was seen to be chewing the fairly fresh remains of a

Red deer (*Cervus elaphus*)

16

Oribi *(Ourebia ouribi)*

rabbit that had died of myxomatosis. In areas where there is a deficiency of calcium in the ground, and therefore in the herbage available for the animals to browse upon, it is well known for deer to eat cast antlers and old bones, which contain necessary calcium.

At the Giza Zoo Gardens a maral, which is a south-west Asian variety of the red deer, made a regular habit of striking down sparrows with a forefoot, and on one occasion it even killed a purple heron that had alighted in its paddock. In 1932, in a Congo National Park a male **oribi** was seen to deliberately strike and kill a dove that was feeding near where they stood. The observer disturbed the buck, which bolted, so was unable to see if it would have eaten the dove, but the killing at least was deliberate.

Other similar observations have been reported for **duikers,** one of which killed a **bustard.**

DUCKS EATING OTHER BIRDS

Apart from a liking for water, ducks and whales would appear to have little in common, yet when a duck dibbles its bill in mud it is doing much the same as when a large whalebone whale opens its huge mouth and charges through a mass of plankton.

Both are using a highly efficient filter. In a duck transverse plates on the inner edges of

Nubian bustard *(Neotis nuba)*

Duiker *(Sylvicapra grimmia)*

Mallard (*Anas platyrhyncha)*

the bill act the part of the baleen plates of the whale, except that the duck's way is more refined.

As the duck dibbles, its tongue acts as a piston sucking water or mud into the mouth and driving it out again. Only edible particles are left behind on the transverse plates, but how the sorting of edible from inedible material is done nobody knows.

Although this is the normal way in which a duck feeds it will also take lumps of bread, as everybody knows who has indulged in the pastime of feeding ducks in the park. If the bread is hard the duck will take it to water and soak it. Ducks also eat insects and their larvae, sometimes tadpoles and worms and even frogs and fish. Occasionally a **mallard** will depart even more widely from this varied diet and will prove to be a real carnivore. There was for example, the occasion when a host of sparrows was feeding in a duck's food trough. The duck came to the trough and struck at one of the sparrows, finally killing it. Then it ate it. It ate 24 sparrows in this way and doubtless would have had more had the sparrows not been disturbed and flown away.

That this is no isolated instance is shown by the several times wild ducks in London parks have been seen to strike at sparrows and to eat them. It happened once when people were feeding the ducks and sparrows on bread. A female mallard joined the group, but apparently not for the bread. She caught a sparrow in her bill, took it to the water and dunked it until it was dead. She then returned to the shore with her meal, ripped the feathers off and devoured the rest.

RABBIT AS FLESH-EATER

When the rabbit population was struck, about six years ago, by the disease known as myxo-

matosis, people were revolted at the abominable symptoms of the disease. Nevertheless, farmers had cause for a sigh of relief when they realized that the enormous damage done to crops by rabbits had come to a sudden and effective end. The scourge of the rabbit is largely due to its being such a complete vegetarian. We normally think of it as a grass eater, but its diet includes many other kinds of plants as well as roots, bark, grain, berries and tubers. In Britain before myxomatosis struck, natural regeneration in forests and orchards was being prevented to an alarming extent by rabbits eating seedlings and young shoots and ring-barking trees. Damage to crops was great and often this was wrongly attributed to insects, poor seed, or exhausted land when, in fact, rabbits were the culprits. A mere handful of rabbits could completely graze down several acres of seedling corn in a week, and continuous grazing often kept as much as a dozen acres continuously bare.

Grassland for pasturing sheep can be as seriously affected. This was especially seen in Australia and New Zealand. Habitually rabbits select the sweetest and the most nutritious grasses and leave the poor weeds untouched. In places, the indigenous grasses have been completely replaced by such weeds and elsewhere their tunnelling near the surface has caused serious soil erosion.

Some figures from New Zealand in the 1880's give point to the gravity of the rabbit problem. During the four-year period there was an increase of 27 per cent in the number of sheep in the province of Canterbury where there were no rabbits. In neighbouring Otago, in the same period, where there was an infestation by

Rabbit (*Oryctolagus cuniculus)*

rabbits, only a 2 per cent increase in the number of sheep was recorded.

But rabbits will sometimes turn flesh-eaters. There are a few instances, all from Ireland, of rabbits eating snails. Piles of empty snailshells have been found outside the entrances to rabbit burrows, sometimes in such quantities as to nearly block the entrance to the burrow. The snails appeared to be brought there singly and eaten at leisure. In addition, tame rabbits have been seen to eat earthworms.

Rabbits, as is well-known, may eat their new-born young if disturbed, thus proving that they can successfully digest animal tissues. This in itself is not, however, evidence of a taste for flesh, but the result of what is called a displacement activity. When an animal experiences conflicting emotions of equal strength its activities become shunted along a line irrelevant to the situation. For example, a bird sitting on her eggs will, if disturbed, have the impulse to fly away but if this is counterbalanced by an equally strong impulse to remain on the nest to protect the eggs, she may go through the motions of tidying the nest, feeding or preening, with no need to tidy the nest, no food to eat, and no need to preen.

The natural instinct for a doe rabbit is to lick her young. If she is alarmed she feels the impulse to run away but the impulse to stay and protect her young counterbalances this. So she does neither and her impulses are channelled into a displacement activity. She eats her young.

PITY THE CARNIVORES

The King of Beasts does not always have it his own way. The **lion** is a powerful animal armed with strong claws and fearsome teeth. To look at him it is hard to believe that the gentle antelope or the zebra could possibly stand any chance when attacked. Yet there are many stories of lions, and more especially lionesses, having been maimed for life by a kick in the teeth from a zebra, or having been fatally impaled on the horns of an antelope.

When the lion or lioness loses its teeth in this way it is apt to become dangerous to human beings because it finds children and women an easy prey, and so many of the man-eaters have been found, when finally they have been tracked down and shot, to have defective teeth either from old age or injury. One African farmer was losing chickens night after night and finally he stayed up and shot the culprit. It was a full-grown lion in its prime with most of its teeth broken, probably from a kick from a zebra.

Perhaps the most pathetic story of animal

Lion (*Panthera leo*)

19

Red fox *(Vulpes vulpes)*

majesty brought low concerns an old lioness in Tanganyika. Both her fangs were broken and she was compelled to kill porcupines to feed her cubs. Her paws were pin-cushioned with porcupine quills and these must have been extremely painful. She was even seen to knock down doves for her cubs and later she tore one of her claws loose trying to tear up an old dried hide to feed to her cubs. It was at this point that a hunter saw her and mercifully despatched her.

FOX'S VARIED DIET

Anyone who has quietly watched a fox on the prowl at night will know the evident caution with which every move is made. Foxes are handsome but shy animals, and have been known to do rather more damage in the farm-yard than can be allowed to pass without comment, despite this animal's handsome appearance and other charms.

Foxes are primarily carnivorous animals as their attacks on chicken-coops would indicate, but it would be a mistake to suppose that they live entirely or even mainly on chickens and rabbits. When myxomatosis struck the rabbit population in England investigations were set afoot in order to find out precisely the normal diet of the red fox. A large number of foxes' stomachs were examined and the first surprise was to find how much grass they ate. It was also found that they ate a large quantity of berries in autumn, and the majority of the stomachs showed very clearly that the basic diet of the **red fox** is mice, voles and rats. The

investigation also showed that a fair quantity of insects are eaten.

Amongst the wide variety of insects found in the stomachs of foxes, beetles seem to predominate along with the remains of ants, earwigs and some remarkable larvae called rat-tailed maggots. Foxes also appear not to be averse to the occasional juicy caterpillar or moth. The indestructible legs and wing-cases taken from the stomachs of foxes enable the expert to identify the species of insects the foxes had been feeding on. Some of the larger ground beetles *(Carabidae)* and dor beetles *(Geotrupidae)* were especially common, with here and there an occasional cockchafer *(Melolontha)*. An unexpected find in the diet of two foxes was that of rat-tailed larvae of the woodland hoverfly *(Myatropa florea)*. These larvae live in stagnant or foul water, or in water caught in cavities in the boles of trees and around the exposed roots of beeches. The "rat-tails" are extensible breathing tubes at the hind end of the maggot's body, which can be pushed to the surface of the water. These rat-tailed maggots may have been eaten deliberately or they may

Red fox *(Vulpes vulpes)*

SPRING & SUMMER mainly BIRDS	SUMMER & AUTUMN mainly INSECTS & FRUIT	AUTUMN & WINTER mainly RODENTS

Thrush

Backbird

Pigeon

Pheasant

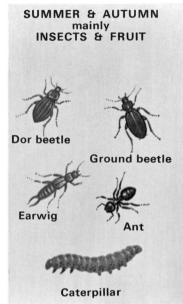

Dor beetle

Ground beetle

Earwig

Ant

Caterpillar

Mouse

Vole

Rat

Rabbit

Basic items in a fox's diet according to the season.

have been lapped up accidentally while the fox was drinking.

We may blame the fox for taking our livestock, but it cannot be gainsaid that foxes in general do a good job in cleaning up carrion, hunting rodent vermin and even devouring maggots, grubs and insects, some of which are noxious pests to the farmer and the forester. That they are by nature partly scavengers is suggested by the way foxes have taken increasingly to living in towns where they raid the garbage bins. In the countryside they search the litter bins for scraps of food thrown away by picnic parties.

IMPORTANCE OF MOTHER'S MILK

Very early in life a child learns the word "bird" and from then on it is never in doubt when it sees a bird. It soon learns to recognize a fish when it sees one, or an insect. And in a few years time it comes to know what a reptile looks like. One of the oddest things about our education is, however, that most of us have only a hazy notion what we should call those animals most closely related to ourselves. To most people they are just plain "animals", and it is only when we come to study zoology more closely that we see the absurdity of the situation. Then we have to learn that these, the highest in the animal scale, are called mammals. Some writers, in searching for a name more easily understood speak of them as the furred animals, because their bodies are covered with hair. But whales are mammals also, and whales are hairless. At best they may have a scattering of bristles on the upper lip, and in most whales even these are lost soon after birth.

Most mammals bear their young alive. But here again there are exceptions. The duckbill or platypus and the half-dozen kinds of spiny anteater, of Australasia, lay eggs.

The only thing they all have in common, and to which there is no exception, is that they feed their babies on mother's milk. Because this is

Dalmatian

21

Flamingo (*Phoenicopterus ruber*)

young on mother's milk during the early days the composition of the milk varies from species to species. This makes a great difference to the rate at which their babies grow. The human baby does not double its weight until it is 180 days old, but a foal doubles its weight in 60 days, a calf in 47 days, a goat-kid in 22 days, a piglet in 14 days, a kitten in 9½ days, a puppy in 9 days and a rabbit in 6 days. The rate of growth is linked with the amount of protein in the mother's milk. In the human mother's milk protein is present as 1.6 grams per cent, and this increases proportionately in the animals named, reaching 10.4 in a rabbit's milk. Even with the first feed the protein in the milk is important. The first flow contains a protein known as cholostrum much of which passes directly through the wall of the stomach into the baby's blood-stream. In the cholostrum are some of the mother's antibodies, and these protect the infant from disease.

Animals other than young mammals do not have the advantage of being able to take their food direct from the mother but must either feed themselves, or be offered solid food by the mother. There are a few exceptions, but whether in these the infant animal receives the added protection from disease is unknown. One of the exceptions is the **flamingo.**

The flamingo chick is fed for two months by both parents with a watery liquid, red in colour secreted by glands situated in the walls of their gullets. It contains red pigments, like

Emperor penguin (*Aptenodytes forsteri*)

conveyed from the mother to the babe through the teat, or mamma, to give it its Greek name, they are called mammals.

One reason why we are justified in calling the mammals the highest in animal creation is that their brain is the largest and most highly organized. This is probably the most important reason. There is, however, another feature of mammals that runs it very close. This is the amount of parental care they receive.

While still in the womb the young mammal is surrounded by a placenta, a fleshy envelope which is in intimate contact with the wall of the womb and through which blood from the mother passes, carrying food for the developing baby. Because of this the young mammal is born in an advanced condition.

Even that is not the end. For a period following birth the baby is nourished with milk, so that it does not need to look for its own food, for days, weeks or months. The mammals that feed babies longest are the hoofed animals. The moose suckles her young for nearly nine months, nearly as long as a cow or a horse. The record is held for the elephant — more than twice as long.

UNUSUAL FOOD OF FLAMINGO CHICKS

Although mammals are animals that feed their

those that colour the flamingo's feathers, and it contains red corpuscles from the parents' blood. The liquid is rich in fat and sugar and the young flamingo thrives exceedingly on it. When hatched a flamingo chick averages 4 ounces but by the time it is 60 days old it weighs anything up to 140 ounces, a remarkably rapid rate of increase. And it is quite possible, although not yet proven, that the flamingo parent may also pass on antibodies to the chick.

PENGUIN MOTHER BRINGS HOME THE FOOD

During the southern winter, which coincides with the summer in the northern hemisphere, the continent of Antarctica experiences temperatures well below freezing point and it is swept by gales and blizzards. The **emperor penguin,** one of the few species to live permanently on this continent, actually lays its eggs during the winter, the period of the most inhospitable weather throughout the whole area. The hen lays only one egg and this is almost immediately taken care of by her mate. She then heads for the open water beyond the pack ice, which may be as much as 200 miles from land, to break her fast, for she will not have eaten for some 7 to 8 weeks before this. The male penguin must continue his fast while he carefully holds the egg on his feet, to keep it off the ice. The best he can do to keep warm

is to huddle with the other male emperor penguins left behind by their mates to care for their eggs.

One of the most remarkable things about the habits of the emperor penguin is this long journey they must make to the open sea to feed. Even more remarkable is the birds' ability to find their way back to the exact spot from which they went, and to do so exactly on time. The egg takes between 62 and 64 days to hatch, and throughout this period the male is holding it and feeding on the fat accumulated in his body. At the end of the time his weight will have dropped by some 30 per cent. Even so, when the egg hatches, he manages to produce a nourishing fluid secreted from glands in his crop to feed the chick for the first day or two. The hen, far out to sea and indulging in an orgy of rich feeding, nevertheless heads back to her mate at the appropriate time, arriving sleek and fat, her crop full of food, ready to take over the feeding of the chick, which thrusts its head into her open beak and takes food from her throat. For a while she assumes full responsibility for the chick while the male heads for the open sea to make good his lost weight. After that they take turns, one going away to feed while the other stays to look after the chick.

SPIDER FEEDS HER BROOD

One of the commonest spiders in gardens

Comb-footed spider *(Theridion sisyphium)*

Drone bee (*Apis mellifera*)

throughout Britain, as well as on heaths, is a species of **comb-footed spider.** It is unique among spiders because the mother actually feeds her young. The adult female spins a web and in mid-June lays a batch of eggs which are protected within a green-blue bag of silk attached to the upper part of the web. The eggs hatch in July and the spiderlings remain with the mother for a few weeks before they disperse and start spinning their own webs and catching their own food.

During the few weeks they are with the mother, she can be seen hanging downwards from her web with the thirty or so spiderlings jostling each other to get near to her mouth. Each is anxious to take its portion of the drop of fluid oozing from the mother's mouth but only two or three can feed at a time. After several days the young are able to take food for themselves, by eating the flies caught in the mother's web.

HEIGHT OF LAZINESS

A colony of bees is made up of one queen, a number of **drones,** and tens of thousands of worker bees. The queen spends her time doing nothing but lay eggs, and she may continue doing this for several years. From time to time during her lifetime she needs to be fertilised afresh, so we find in the hive anything up to several hundred males, during the summer. They are called drones because they do nothing except fertilise the queen when the need for this arises — and only one is needed for that! The purpose of so many hundreds ensures that when the queen needs fertilising there will be at least one surviving to do this whatever the circumstances. The drones do nothing else for their living and are even fed by the worker bees. Only very occasionally will one wander over to help himself from the honey cells in the comb. The drones spend three-quarters

of their time doing nothing more than this and only occasionally do they fly out of the hive. Although the drones are fed by the workers the experienced bees do not waste their time on them, so the drones are fed mainly by worker bees four to six days old, almost as if the young workers were serving an apprenticeship before passing on to the more essential duties connected with the hive.

INSATIABLE PRAYING MANTIS

The different species of **praying mantis** differ mainly in size, from less than an inch to five inches long. All have the same method of feeding. They remain perfectly still on a plant, clinging by the second and third pairs of legs, the first pair held up and folded upon themselves, in an attitude almost of supplication. The two outer joints of the folded front legs bear spines and with them the mantis can grip its prey as in the jaws of a gin-trap. Over and

Praying mantis (*Mantis religiosa*)

above this efficient natural trap a mantis possesses a disposition in which moderation, even fear, have no part. The usual prey is other insects, of any kind, and mantises seem to be able to eat insects that are unpalatable to other animals by reason of their poisons. A mantis under test has eaten insects flavoured with ammonia or with prussic acid. Nor does the mantis confine its attentions to insects. Frogs and lizards share the same fate, even birds up to sparrow-size are not safe from the larger man-

Koala (*Phascolarctos cinereus*)

tises, and small snakes have been killed by these gin-trap insects, which will ´attack animals twenty times their own bulk even if they are, in the end, unable to hold them. One mantis was seen to have gripped a shrew and was biting into its neck, and others have been seen to show fight to kittens, and it is not the mantis that retreats.

KOALAS BITE THE DUST

In contrast to the omnivores there are animals with a restricted diet. They are usually spoken of as specialized feeders because they eat more especially one particular kind of food and the best example among the furred animals is the **koala,** often spoken of as the Australian Teddy Bear. It is not a true bear but a marsupial or pouched animal, distantly related to the kangaroo.

Koalas used to be very numerous indeed but their numbers have been severely reduced, partly because at one time they were killed by the million for their skins, but in later years the danger has been the cutting down of eucalyptus forests. Koalas eat only eucalyptus leaves. Moreover, they are said to eat only eucalyptus leaves before these have grown too old. It is because of their specialized diet that koalas cannot be kept in European zoos, since there are no eucalyptus trees from which to feed them. A few years ago it was noticed that some of the koalas in Australia were dying off and

autopsy showed that they were dying of a disease. Many of the koalas examined in the autopsies had gravel in the caecum, the blind tube leading from the small intestine which in ourselves we call the appendix. Australian zoologists had also noticed that koalas, which spend all their time in the trees, occasionally came down to the ground to eat soil, presumably to correct a mineral deficiency in their diet. Unfortunately, the soil also contains a fungus and this, it is believed, is responsible for the disease.

NATURE'S MORTICIANS

Travellers in Africa have always been surprised at the speed with which a carcase, even of so

Flesh-eating flies (*Sarcophagidae* sp.)

25

large an animal as an elephant, disappears. Anything remaining after the lions, hyaenas and vultures have finished with it is next attacked by rodents and finally insects. We have to go to North America, however, for precise experiments on this.

In a series of experiments carried out in the United States, it was found that insects are chiefly responsible for the way carcases of dead animals are so quickly reduced to nothing but a skeleton.

For these experiments piglets born dead, or accidentally crushed by the sow, were used. These were preserved by freezing until enough had been collected, then they were divided into two groups. All were placed in a wooded area, but one group was merely laid on the ground so that insects and other living organisms could easily reach them, while the other group was covered up so that nothing could get to them. Within five minutes, **flesh-eating flies** arrived on the scene and started work on the carcases to which they had free access. Many of the insects laid their eggs on the dead piglets almost as soon as they arrived on the scene. These eggs soon hatched and the grubs from them started to feed on the flesh, so helping the adult flies in the cleaning and disintegration process. There were 422 different kinds of insects taking part in this work. Eight days after the experiment started only dry skin, gristle and bone were left. At the end of three weeks all that remained was hair, bits of skin, bones and teeth. But the decay and decomposition of the piglets free from insects was very different. At first they became bloated, then they started to dry up, until after several days they had reached a mummified state that lasted as much as two months. At the end of three months, when the experiments finished, the shape of the body was still well defined and easily recognizable.

In temperate climates, at least, it seems that rapid reduction of dead animals to skeletons is mainly the work of insects, partly by their feeding, breeding and burrowing activities, but also because they carry bacteria, which also help in the process of disintegration. The bones remaining may be gnawed by rats and other rodents, or else they become covered by leaf-litter and are, in due course, buried.

Quite incidentally to this story is the fact that rats are incurable gnawers of bones and they leave on the ends of long bones, the marks of their teeth. Archaeologists, unearthing such bones, have sometimes been misled into sup-

Rook (*Corvus frugilegus*)

posing prehistoric man had worked these patterns on bone, as a sort of primitive art.

GRAIN IS AN ACQUIRED TASTE IN ROOKS

Archaeologists are not the only people to be misled by animals' feeding habits.

A certain farmer had had on his land some large elms for many years in which there was a rookery. The elms bordered a field of arable land but the farmer had not been bothered at all from the **rooks** raiding his crops. One season the rook population became doubled and the birds were seen invading the field of grain in force. In fear for his crop-yield the farmer shot many rooks. Now comes the question: was the farmer sure that the rooks were actually eating his grain?

Rooks store food in their crops before fully digesting it, so in order to answer this question some of the dead birds' crops were examined. It was found that 75 per cent of the birds had eaten no grain at all, they had been feeding exclusively on wireworms and other insects that do enormous damage to crops. Of the remaining 25 per cent each bird had taken about half grain and half insects. A favourite food of rooks is cockchafer grubs, with leatherjackets and wireworms a close second, and it is reasonable to expect that when these insects have all been eaten the next nearest food is the grain. So it would be surprising if the rooks took no grain at all.

The fact is that on average rooks are likely to do more good than harm to crops by picking off the harmful insects. And this seems borne out by the way these birds treat their food.

A rook in captivity, hand-reared as a fledgling so that it has never learned how other rooks behave, will when offered cockchafer grubs for the first time readily accept them. The bird immediately bites off the insect's head bearing strong jaws, and then pecks off the scratchy

Rook (*Corvus frugilegus*)

legs. Only then, when the grub has been rendered absolutely harmless does the rook peck into and consume the juicy parts of its body. The important point in this is that a young rook that has been hand-reared away from all other rooks will treat a cockchafer in this way the first time it has one, and will always do so whenever one of these insects is presented to it. This shows that its action in dismembering the jaws and legs of the insect is instinctive. By contrast, a young rook brought up in this same isolation when given grain for the first time will look at it for a moment then pick up a grain and try to smash it, treating it as if it were an insect which had to be rendered harmless. Only later does it learn that the grain is good to eat and each grain can be swallowed whole.

Even if there were no other evidence, such as the examination of the crops of dead rooks, we could suspect from the way a hand-reared rook knows instinctively how to deal with insects, but has to learn how to cope with grain, that insects are its primary food. One can only report therefore that it is highly likely that on balance rooks do far more good than harm to the farmer.

At the least, it is of interest to find this difference between an instinctive pattern of feeding where large insects are concerned and the need for the rook to learn to eat grain.

A CRICKET EXONERATED

An insect long blamed for crop-damage has recently been exonerated by more careful research. It has long been thought that mole crickets are a pest to plants because they eat

Mole cricket (*Gryllotalpa vulgaris*)

Red deer *(Cervus elaphus)*

the roots of plants. This insect is related to the house cricket but lives a burrowing life, like the more familiar furred animal after which it is named. Another point of interest is that there is a strong resemblance between the flattened spadelike fore-paws of a mole and the flattened front legs of the mole cricket.

A few years ago a German scientist made a close investigation of the feeding habits of the **mole cricket** and, as so often proves the case, found that a rooted belief was unfounded. According to his observations on captive mole crickets these insects will take insect food such as caterpillars and earthworms in preference to vegetable food. More careful research by the same scientist revealed that a fully-grown cricket would eat 10 per cent of its own body weight of insects in 15 minutes, but would take 24 hours to eat the same weight of plant tissues, almost as if it were putting up with the plant food on sufferance.

There is the chance that mole crickets may be a pest to plants when they are present in large numbers in an area of soil. Then, some of them may be forced to eat roots because there are not enough insects, of the kind they eat, to go round. It is likely, also, that in their tunnelling they may interfere with or damage the roots of seedlings, even when feeding on

insects. But the fact seems now to be established that on balance mole crickets do more good than harm to crops by helping to clear the soil of insect vermin.

DANGER OF FEEDING DEER IN WINTER

Being able to obtain the right kind of food may be of fundamental importance. One example of this is seen in the **red deer**. This species, with its many subspecies, extends across Europe and Asia, and a close relative, the wapiti, is found in North America.

Many years ago workmen discovered a large staircase in Hampton Court Palace on the outskirts of London. Hampton Court had been a royal palace in Tudor times. Until the twentieth century nobody knew the staircase was there because its two entrances had been walled up. Apparently, at some time, it had been used as a dump for the heads and antlers of red deer shot by the royal hunting parties. Possibly they had been cleared out from other parts of the palace when Sir Christopher Wren started to re-build it. The important point about these antlers was that they were noticeably larger than the antlers of deer living today in Britain. There is a simple explanation of this.

Red deer are browsers not grazers. A browser is an animal that lives on leaves and twigs. A grazer is an animal that eats grass or very low herbage on the ground. Deer are mainly browsers and to some extent grazers in winter. In the 16th century and earlier huge forests covered much of Britain and the red deer could browse to their heart's content. With the Industrial Revolution much of this forest was cut down and the land turned over to agriculture. Roaming red deer were forced to become mainly grazers, with the result that red deer in Britain today are markedly smaller than those living in the forests in Europe and especially in eastern Europe. Furthermore, it is noticeable that the red deer in the mountains of the Scottish Highlands, where trees and bushes are even more scarce, are much smaller than those that live in the lowlands where there is a richer vegetation. The average Highland stag weighs 210 lbs., an English woodland stag may weigh as much as 420 lbs., while those from the more extensive woodlands of eastern Europe may weigh as much as 560 lbs., and the size of the antlers varies in proportion.

In winter the leaves and twigs are in short supply and the deer must become mainly grazers, and it is then that, in England, they are likely to suffer from hunger. To offset this people sometimes put dry hay out for the deer, but this amounts to almost a kindness that kills because a starving deer cannot digest hay which forms a fibrous ball in its stomach. Even a healthy deer cannot be adequately maintained on a diet of hay alone, without becoming liable

Roe deer *(Capreolus capreolus)*

to parasites and disease. Winter is a time of natural erosion of deer populations, when many die of hunger. It is a natural check on their numbers, necessary because too many deer in one place soon destroy their own habitat so that the whole population suffers. However lamentable the death of deer may seem, under the restricted conditions of their habitat in overcrowded Britain, feeding hay to starving deer seems not to improve their lot.

FASTIDIOUS DEER

The **sika deer** was first made known to science in 1838. It inhabits Japan and large areas of Siberia and China. It was introduced into parks in the British Isles in the mid-nineteenth century, from which it has escaped and become feral in many places for at least 70 years. Yet despite this long history all we could say about its food was that it ate grass and herbs, and

Sika deer *(Cervus nippon)*

Long-beaked dolphin(*Sousa teuszi*)

sometimes bark.

Research in 1966 has shown how complicated are the feeding habits of sika, and this probably holds good for other deer. They feed at night, but apparently irregularly, since in one place there may be 6 deer one night and 60 the next. They eat mainly grass, but will not feed where sheep have been. They feed more from December to April than during the rest of the year. And they ignore some fields although these have identical soil and grass to those they favour, yet roe and fallow deer quite happily graze the fields the sika ignore.

LIGHT FEEDER

Grass feeders have large bellies because they need to consume large quantities of food to obtain sufficient nourishment. A cow is a good example of this kind of herbivore. Deer are also herbivores but they are browsers, which means they feed largely on leaves and on vegetation other than grass. They do not need to consume the same huge quantities as the grazers, and this is brought out by what we know of the roe deer. A **roe deer** may weigh up to 60 lbs., and it eats only 3 to 4 per cent of its own weight daily, of leaves and berries, tender shoots and clover. For a full-grown roe this means at most $2\frac{1}{2}$ lbs. of food a day.

MYSTERY DOLPHIN

In 1892 a **long-beaked dolphin** was found lying dead on the beach of the Cameroon River in West Africa. It was about 6 feet long and the remarkable thing was that its stomach was filled with leaves, grass and mangrove fruits. For over 60 years this dolphin has been regarded as the only herbivorous species of whale. It was also regarded as a rare species simply because only this one specimen had ever been found. In 1956 matters took a different turn. Owing to the researches of two French scientists it was then found not only that this dolphin was a fish-eater but also that it was very common, and in the years 1958 to 1959 it was seen almost daily from January to early April, by the two French scientists, especially at low tide, in the rivers and estuaries in Senegal. The mystery still remains why that original specimen had its stomach filled with vegetation. One suggestion is that this vegetable material had come from the stomachs of fish eaten by the dolphin. Even this seems unlikely and we may have to wait further for a real explanation.

MYTH OF THE KILLER WHALE

Killer whales are known as the wolves of the sea because they hunt in packs and eat almost any kind of animal thay can catch, including porpoises and dolphins, seals and sea birds. In addition, they will attack the very large whales, biting lumps of blubber out of their bodies. The picture we have of killer whales is of relentless hunters with an almost limitless capacity to swallow food. This picture has been enhanced by the telling and re-telling of the story of a 24-foot killer whale whose stomach was found to contain 13 porpoises and 14 seals. A look at the picture on this page shows that for such a thing to happen it would need to be very near to a miracle. In fact, it would be impossible. The truth is that the first person to record what was found in the stomach of this killer whale said that the stomach contained the remains of 13 porpoises and 14 seals, the remains of several meals. Subsequently other writers were so impressed with this that they retailed the story but omitted the words "remains of", and so the story came to read that the killer whale's stomach contained 13 porpoises and 14 seals, which was spectacular but not strictly accurate.

THE FOOD OF QUEENS

Perhaps the classic example of how food can affect the lives of individuals is found in the honeybee. It is common knowledge that the young queens in a beehive come from the same kind of eggs as the worker bees and that they become queens because they are fed on a special food known as royal jelly. This was discovered in 1888 by a German scientist, and as so often happens the story has been told again and again until it becomes almost household knowledge. In the last 20 years, however, there has been very intensive research on the honeybee. One result of this is to show that this old story about the royal jelly is not strictly correct, although we are still not certain what the whole truth of it may be.

We know that the eggs destined to give rise to queens are laid in special cells whereas those destined to give rise to workers are laid in the ordinary honeycomb cells. The special queen cells are much larger and they hang vertically from the comb. Because the queen cells are much larger they will hold more food so that the growing grub that hatches from the egg has a superabundance of food. In fact, when the queen grub has pupated and after the young queen has left the cell there is invariably some food still left. It is very different with the worker grubs which are not only living in smaller cells but are given a limited ration of food by the

Killer whale *(Orcinus orca)*

31

Honeybee (*Apis mellifera*)

nurse bees every day. However, it has been shown that if you take a grub from a worker cell and give it an excess of food it still does not become a queen, so clearly something more is needed than a superabundance of food. During the first three days in the life of a grub destined to become a queen the nurse bees feed it with a special food that is milky-white instead of being clear and it is believed, although not fully proven, that this contains a certain amount of fluid from the nurse bees' salivary glands. Whether this is a hormone, a vitamin or what, cannot yet be said. What is known is that it must be given during the first three days of the grub's life. For example, if a queen grub is artificially fed for the first three days and then put in the care of a nurse bee it will not grow into a queen because the essential food will then have been given to it too late in life.

CONNOISSEUR'S CHOICE

You might be excused for supposing that the best-flavoured mutton comes from sheep that have fed on the best pastures. In England, at least, it is believed that a snail contributes most to the superior flavour of South Down and Dartmoor mutton. **Sheep** are basically herbivores, yet it is claimed that if, in a pasture, there is one area richer in **snails** than elsewhere the sheep will automatically make for it. In some places these snails are very numerous, so much so that after rain they are seen in such vast numbers, drawn from their hiding places by the moisture, that there have been sensational reports of showers of snails. Whether they eat the snails as such or take them into their mouths with the grass is really beside the point. The sheep actually consume the snails, and this it is believed imparts the special flavour of the mutton they yield.

BIRDS SOFTENING FOOD

Having a bird-table within easy sight of the house affords great pleasure to the spectator. A variety of scraps can be put out for the birds, but probably the most usual food is stale bread and crusts. There have been several instances of birds finding crusts too hard to eat, so they deliberately soften them in water. **House-sparrows** have been seen to take crusts to a bird-bath, drop them in the water, and wait a few seconds before taking them out. By that time the outside of the crust is easy to peck away and the sparrows feed either themselves or their young with it, often abandoning the inside part which may still be hard. **Gulls** too have been seen dunking bread in the sea both in England and in Australia. A **carrion crow** was seen to dabble bread in a bird-bath with its beak, rather as a duck dabbles amongst weeds,

Snail (*Helix virgata*)
Domestic sheep (*Ovis* sp.)

then to push the soft bread across the bird-bath to a large fledgling. On another occasion a crow brought crusts from elsewhere to a water tin, and when he had softened them sufficiently, flew up into a tree to eat them. There is one record of a **jay** using water to soften its food, and another of a crow making use of a puddle on a golf-course as a convenient dunking place. It has been suggested that this sensible action by the birds is more likely to result from their imitating each other. Even if this were true we would have to suppose that there was a bird that originally departed from its normal feeding behaviour to the point of working out how to soften the bread. To say the least, these simple and everyday observations of birds in the garden suggest that birds have at least a limited power of reasoning, an ability to put one and one together even if they are unable to put two and two together.

HOW WALRUSES FEED

The **walrus,** one of the largest of seals, inhabits the arctic seas. The male is slightly larger than the female and may measure up to 16 feet in length with a weight of just over a ton. The walrus muzzle is broad and blunt and its upper lip is thickened in two firm fleshy pads either side of the nostrils, known as moustachial pads. Each pad bears stout bristly whiskers. Another feature of the walrus is that both male and female have long ivory tusks up to 2 feet in length. They look like formidable weapons and no doubt can be used as such. We are told, also, that the walrus sometimes uses them to haul itself out onto ice-floes. But the main use of the tusks is in grubbing for food on the sea-bed. The walrus dives, anything up to a depth of 120 feet and rakes the sandy bed of the sea with its tusks to stir up crabs, molluscs and sea-urchins living in it. The lips and the whiskers are used to sort out the food, which is then dealt with according to what it is. For example, a mussel will be taken into the mouth and cracked and the soft parts of its body sucked out and swallowed. The shell is then spat out. Larger shellfish, as well as crabs and sea-urchins, may be broken by a sharp blow from the moustachial pad and then the soft contents sucked out. The full story of how walruses feed is only imperfectly known. Wild walruses have, for example, been observed digging over the sea-bed with their tusks. Young walruses have been watched in captivity and seen to crack shells with their moustachial pads. But most of what we know comes from the examination of the stomachs of dead walruses. This tells us what they feed on. It also tells us that they do not swallow shells, as a rule, because these have only rarely been found in the stomachs. So the usual method of feeding seems to be to suck in their food. Even when eating a fish a walrus will hold it with its flippers and suck in the flesh from it into its mouth. Walruses will also eat the flesh of dead seals, although how exactly they do this is not known, and Frank Buckland has set on record, in the latter part of the 19th century, the story from a whaling captain of a fight between a **narwhal** and a walrus. Both animals were killed by the whalers and when the narwhal was hauled on board it was found to have been disembowelled,

Herring gull (*Larus argentatus*)

House sparrow (*Passer domesticus*)

Carrion crow (*Corvus corone*)

Mallard (*Anas platyrhyncha*)

Ducks also soften food.

and much of its blubber had been eaten away. That this was the work of the walrus was confirmed when that animal was examined. It had narwhal flesh in its stomach. It is belie-ved that the walrus had come upon the sleeping narwhal, had swung underneath it, had dug its tusks into the narwhal's belly, and had then held onto it with its flippers while it proceeded to make a meal of it. Another puzzle connected with walruses is that any walrus stomach cut open is found to contain a number of pebbles. It is usually said that these pebbles form a sort of mill, that they are rubbed together by the contraction of the stomach muscles, and there-fore are used for crushing the food in the stomach. Yet, if walruses feed mainly by sucking in soft foods this hardly seems neces-sary. Pebbles are found in the stomachs of other animals, for example, the crocodile, and there the suggestion is that they are used as ballast to keep the crocodile on an even keel. Horses also sometimes swallow pebbles, and there are indications that some prehistoric reptiles also did so. The whole story of pebbles in animals' stomachs still needs a satisfactory explanation because the reason given for one animal seldom fits for another and altogether, we are very much in the dark on this.

OWLS' FAMILIES ARE REGULATED BY FOOD

The recommendation that there should be widespread use of birth-control to limit the populations in under-developed countries, faced

Walrus (*Odobenus rosmarus*)
Narwhal (*Monodon monoceros*)

with a serious shortage of food, may be an idea new to man, but many birds and animals have been doing something similar for millions of years. The only difference is that with man birth-control is deliberate, while with animals it is governed largely by the food supply. The breeding of the **snowy owl** and the **hawk owl** appears to relate directly to the abundance or otherwise of food. One of the chief food items of these species is the lemming, a small rodent living in Scandinavia and in arctic Canada. As is well known the populations of lemmings fluctuate greatly, in cycles of 3 to 10 years. In years when they are particularly numerous, in what are called " good lemming years", these owls may lay up to 13 eggs each, which is nearly double the normal number. As a rule both these species lay 4 or 5 eggs, but the number tends to fluctuate somewhat between these figures and 9 or 10 eggs to a clutch, giving a general average of seven. In years when there are very few lemmings they may not nest at all. Another feature of owls is their "staggered" birth. This is thought to be a means of survival in carnivorous birds, to cope with possible shortage of prey. As soon as one egg is laid, the owls start to incubate, laying more eggs later. This means that the hatching of the nestlings is spread over a long period, so that although the parents have to find food for their young for a longer period than if all hatched more or less together, as is normal in most birds, they never have to find so large a

Walrus (*Odobenus rosmarus*)

35

Hawk owl (*Surnia ulula*)

Snowy owl (*Nyctea scandiaca*)

JAYS FIND HIDDEN FOOD

The common jay eats a wide variety of foods, from insects to fruit, as well as eggs and flesh. But in autumn, when the acorns ripen, it will gorge itself with these. It holds each acorn under one foot, neatly strips off the husk with its beak and eats the kernel. Even a jay hand-reared in an aviary, that has never seen another jay eating an acorn, will not only readily accept it as food but will know exactly how to husk it. Any other member of the crow family, given an acorn, will pull it to pieces, but will do so clumsily, and will not necessarily eat the kernel. In addition to the autumn feasting the jay will bury acorns, much in the way a squirrel will bury them. The jay flies off with an acorn in its beak, drops to the ground, lays the acorn down and pecks a hole with its beak. It then picks up the acorn, drops it in the hole and covers it with earth.

A squirrel will find a nut or acorn it has buried, guided to the spot by its sense of smell.

quantity at any one time as they would if all the nestlings were growing up together.

BLACKBIRDS CATCH FISH

Keeping goldfish in ornamental ponds has long been a favourite pastime in many parts of the world. Wherever there are fish ponds there will come fish-eating birds to prey upon them. Kingfishers and herons are the main culprits, but it will sometimes happen that in a city park or garden where no herons or kingfishers live, a fish pond starts to lose its fish. They gradually disappear for no apparent reason. On several occasions the culprits have been caught red-handed. In one instance it was a starling, in another instance it was a **blackbird** that had raided the fish pond. There was a trout hatchery that became the object of attention by blackbirds. Apparently, one blackbird went to it to drink, saw the trout fry swim past and learned that this was an easy method of obtaining a meal, so it repeated it. The following year numerous blackbirds came to take the fish. It can only be supposed that they were following the example of the original blackbird, but in the end they took so many trout fry that the owner of the hatchery was faced with the alternative of either shooting the blackbirds or going out of business.

Blackbird (*Turdus merula*)

A **jay** does it by sight. It can fly straight to the spot, even weeks later, and dig up an acorn.

There is no hesitation in its movements, which show that it remembers exactly where it has buried the acorn. Even more remarkable, it will do the same when thick snow covers the ground.

SO DO OTHER BIRDS

The marsh tit, a small brown bird with a black cap, varies its food with the season. For much of the year it feeds on all manner of insects, but as autumn sets in and insects become scarce it turns to seeds and berries, and particularly to beech mast. It will sometimes come to the bird-table to feed, and then we can see how its habits differ from most of the other birds feeding there.

While they are busy eating the food on the spot, or squabbling amongst themselves over it, the marsh tit will take a piece of food and fly away. It will be back again in a few seconds to repeat this, and if we watch it carefully we shall see it make scores of such journeys in a few minutes. Now, if we watch where it goes to we see that each time it flies away it lands on the branch or trunk of a tree and presses the morsel of food into a crevice in the bark, before flying back for more.

Marsh tits do the same in the wild, storing bits of food, from the beech mast and berries, in the cracks in the bark. However, they do not lose sight of this stored food, or if they do they can still come back to it. Tests have shown that if the bark is covered up, as it might be by snow in winter, marsh tits will come back to the exact spot where food was cached to retrieve it.

STORES OF FAT

Voles are mouse-like but they differ from house mice, and other true mice, in having a blunter muzzle, smaller eyes and smaller ears.

Most voles are wholly vegetarian and some of them can be plagues to crops such as meadow grass.

They do, however, take a certain amount of insect food and it is fairly certain that it is attractive to them because of the amount of fatty or oily material in the insects. Even while knowing this, a naturalist was surprised one day to find the carcase of a fox which, as he watched, was moving as if it contained huge beetles feeding inside it. He found **meadow voles** were feeding on the fat in it and so anxious were they to stuff themselves with the fat that as fast as he pulled them away and set them on the ground they staggered back to their feeding places as if unable to resist this unexpected and, to them, tremendous store of fat that had suddenly come their way.

OILING THE WORKS

The petroleum fly is a small, shiny black fly that lives in the oilfields of southern California and, as was discovered a few years ago, in those of Trinidad. The larvae live solely in the pools of thick crude oil, a habitat that would be fatal to any other insect.

Indeed, they feed on insects that have become trapped in the oil, swimming strongly through the thick fluid to reach then. The adult fly walks with impunity on the surface of the oil. When eating, **petroleum flies** take in a fair quantity of oil with their food, but most of this does not pass through the wall of the gut and into their system, although small quantities must get through, judging by tests in the

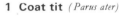
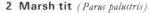

1 **Coat tit** (*Parus ater*)
2 **Marsh tit** (*Parus palustris*)

Jay (*Garrulus glandarius*)

Meadow vole (*Microtus agrestis*)

C in its diet. All insects that had been studied up to that time were found to manufacture their own Vitamin C inside their bodies, or rather all insects contained bacteria or yeasts in their gut

Petroleum fly (*Psilopa petrolei*)

Locust (*Schistocerca gregaria*)

laboratory.

In these tests it was found that the adult flies would not lay eggs so long as they were not allowed access to oil, but would do so once oil was made available to them, and even a mere trace was sufficient to bring them into breeding condition.

LOCUSTS MUST BE FASTIDIOUS

We give babies and young children orange juice because it contains vitamins, notably Vitamin C, that are essential for their growth and well-being. Animals need their vitamins too. Diets which are deficient in some essential substance can have serious consequences to the animal concerned as it can to a human being.

For example, it has been discovered that young **locusts** need Vitamin C quite as much as do young humans. As far as is known it helps these insects in their moulting, and if they are artificially fed on a diet deficient in this vitamin they rarely survive to become adults, and those that do survive are usually malformed and short-lived. As a rule they die after the last moult, which is the last stage between the larva and the adult.

It has also been said with regard to flies (but this is rather a general statement and as such must be treated carefully), that the diet of the adults often makes up for deficiencies inherent in the diet of the larvae. That is, if a larva is carnivorous, the adult is likely to feed on plants and vice versa. A good example of this is one particular species of mosquito. This has carnivorous larvae, but the adult, in contrast to most other mosquitoes, feeds on flowers.

What makes the discovery about locusts' diet so interesting is that only a few years ago it was thought that no insect needed to take in Vitamin

that manufactured the Vitamin C from the things the insect ate. By contrast, the locust must take in Vitamin C actually in its food and this is contained in the plants on which it normally feeds.

OPPORTUNISTS: AMERICAN VULTURES

Vultures are by nature birds that obtain an easy living by scavenging the carcases of animals that die in the open. They are well-known for their habit of soaring high in the skies out of sight and then dropping down from the skies, one after another as soon as an animal falls dead, to cluster round the carcase to feast on it. On the big highways of the southern United States the **turkey vulture** and the **black vulture** have learned how to get an even easier living. They now appreciate that animals crossing the road are liable to be knocked down and killed by vehicles travelling at speed, and many of these vultures take up station along the highways and wait for their food to be conveniently provided for them by the death-dealing human traffic.

OPPORTUNISTS: BRITISH GULLS

Those responsible for looking after Admiral Nelson's flagship, H.M.S. *Victory,* lying in her concrete cradle at Portsmouth dockyard, have long noted that gulls do not perch anywhere on the ship nor is any part of the ship fouled by their droppings. A short while ago somebody tried to find a possible explanation by consulting various experts on birds, for although the *Victory* is unmolested there are plenty of **gulls** practical was that it was all a matter of food. Gulls are by nature beggars. They will readily flock to places along the shore where people picnic daily. They will congregate there and wait for the human visitors. H.M.S. *Victory* is always kept spick and span and it is difficult to imagine any visitor or any of its custodians eating sandwiches or consuming food while on board. So there is no food for the gulls, not even a few crumbs. If we look at other histori-

Turkey vulture *(Cathartes aura)*

Black vulture *(Coragyps atratus)*

elsewhere in the dockyard. The experts were somewhat puzzled to account for this and gave a variety of explanations. Perhaps the most cal ships moored in rivers or harbours, kept there as interesting relics and always kept clean, we find the same absence of gulls.

Herring gull *(Larus argentatus)*

39

Domestic fowl *(Gallus gallus)*

BIRDS SOCIAL FEEDING

Besides the effect on growth, bodily size and on the breeding of animals, food can have a social importance, almost constituting a means of communication. We say "Birds of a feather flock together" and birds of a feather do literally flock together, especially when they belong to a species that feeds socially. That is, they feed in flocks. It now seems, from researches made recently, that the instinct giving rise to social feeding can be traced to its origin in the chick of the **domestic fowl,** a species in which social feeding is well developed.

When chicks aged between 16-24 hours were shown a model of a hen's head they instinctively pecked at it, mostly at the beak. When a small ball was attached to the tip of the model's beak they transferred their attention to this. They almost completely ignored the eye on the model although it was of the same size and colour as the ball. So it was not the ball itself that mattered so much as its position in relation to the rest of the head. Consequently, a chick standing near a hen as she lowers her head will

Honeybee *(Apis mellifera)*

instinctively move to peck at her beak. Then, as her beak touches a grain of food there will be an even greater impulse on the part of the chick to peck at that. So the chick starts to learn what is food. Similarly, when a mechanical model of a hen was made to peck at grains of two different colours, the chicks that were near it usually pecked at the same coloured grains as the "parent" model had selected.

As is usual with other animals most birds seem to be attracted to their own kind, especially so when feeding. Tests on chaffinches and sparrows indicated that they seemed to be attracted even to other species of birds that were feeding, and that the young birds of these two species would feed not only on familiar foods but also on unfamiliar foods so long as they had seen other birds doing so first!

Because young birds follow the example of older birds in their feeding habits it helps to ensure that they obtain the correct kinds of food.

BEES' FOOD-SHARING

A feature of the behaviour of the **honeybee** which was early noted by bee keepers was their habit of sharing food. Foraging bees coming back to the hive, carrying pollen and nectar in their crops, pass this on to the household bees, those that stay behind to do the chores in the hive. Some of this is eventually turned into honey in the household bees crop and any excess is then stored. Some of the food is used to feed the growing grubs in the comb. Some is used to feed the members of the hive, and this is done by two bees coming together, mouth to mouth, the one disgorging food into the other's mouth.

The workers also feed the queen and they receive from her a secretion known as the queen substance. Not only is the nectar and pollen passed around from one bee to another but bees receiving the queen's substance then pass it to other members of the hive. It is not quite clear yet how far this communal feeding imparts a common odour to all the bees in a colony. There is a suspicion that it to some extent explains how strange bees are recognized and either refused admission or ejected after entry into a hive. It is also likely that bees of the same hive recognize each other by their odour. So communal feeding is to some extent a means of communication, as well as a means of ensuring that all members of a hive are adequately fed.

The introduction of queen substance into food

Social spider *(Agelena consociata)*

shared also keeps the bees aware that the queen is in occupation of the hive and therefore they go about their duties contentedly. Should the queen bee be removed, and the queen substance be no longer available, the worker bees become aware of this and become disturbed. This leads them to take action to remedy it.

FOOD-SWAPPING SPIDERS

Exchange of food between members of a society or colony of insects seems to be fairly common practice. We would not expect to find it among spiders because these are mainly solitary animals. There is, however, a highly **social spider** in tropical Africa which forms organized communities. Each community builds an extensive web with galleries and chambers and anything killed is shared by the members of the colony. The mouth of these spiders is so constructed that digestion of the food must take place outside. The spider injects gastric juices into its prey which liquidizes it. Since all members of the spider community set to work on an insect carcase the resulting semi-liquid mass contains saliva from them all. When they start to suck in the liquid mass each takes in some portion of the saliva contributed by its fellows. We could not be certain of this but for the use of radio-active substances. By injecting a radio-active isotope into two crickets

and then allowing two spiders each to feed on one of the crickets these two spiders became "labelled". Three days later the labelled spiders were then allowed to feed in company with eight of their fellow spiders that were unlabelled and their prey was a cricket which contained no radio-active isotope. After the meal all the spiders were found to be radio-active.

DEMOCRATIC HUNTING DOGS

Cape hunting dogs are sturdy and long-legged with broad heads and large ears, and a coat which is blotched black, white and yellow. They move about in packs, running down game, the pack keeping together by uttering soft hooting sounds. These sounds are merely a means of letting each member of the pack know where the others are at a given moment because a hunting dog pack is a very close-knit community. All members of the pack show a marked tolerance towards each other, the only disagreements between them being of a very minor nature. Moreover, they have a communal feeding system.

When the members of the pack return from a hunting foray with their stomachs full of food, then begins the process of sharing out the food. Each disgorges its share and both adults and pups partake of this. Not only that but the food is swallowed and disgorged several times so that a piece of meat wanders through several stomachs before being finally digested. In the hunting dogs, therefore, the stomach is used first as a receptacle for the transport of food, to take it into cover where it can be eaten at leisure. But it is not digested until after the ceremony of passing it from one to the other has been performed.

Cape hunting dog *(Lycaon pictus)*

BATS' PUMP-AND-FILTER

In Trinidad lives the **lattice-winged bat,** so-called because clear bands of skin in the wings produce a lattice-like effect. A lattice is, strictly speaking, a kind of network and it would be more appropriate to call this bat a lattice-mouthed bat because of the remarkable filtering apparatus on its lips. However, the filter does not stop there and in considering the whole of the bat's apparatus we have a most remarkable example of an animal that feeds on soft fruit pulp and juice using a natural suction and filter.

This bat, which has one of the ugliest faces of a group of animals noted for their ugly faces, is otherwise quite harmless, except to crops of fruit. It feeds on the over-ripe and mushy parts of bananas and paw-paws, and although it has teeth these are not as strongly developed as in other bats. These weak teeth may possibly be

Lattice-winged bat *(Centurio senex)*

used for tearing open the fruit, although nobody has seen them do this, but they could equally well be used as strainers to supplement those on the lips. The skin between the bat's lips and gums is covered with numerous fleshy papillae. A papilla might be best described as a conical pimple and it seems fairly certain that the bat sucks fruit juice or mushy pulp through the half-closed mouth with the papillae straining off any large pieces.

The bat's throat is extremely tiny, no more than one twelfth of an inch across. Since the bat itself has a wing-span of about 12 inches and a head the size of a ping-pong ball, this is a very, very small throat indeed. Behind this throat opening the gullet leads backwards but has a second opening of about the same size, and

behind this second opening is a kind of bag leading out from the wall of the gullet which seems to act as a kind of sucking apparatus.

Some people advocate that to keep healthy we should chew all our food until it is almost liquid. The lattice-winged bat, instead of keeping a good set of teeth such as most bats possess, has in an evolutionary sense allowed its teeth to become weak and has gone to the trouble of developing a quite remarkable apparatus to ensure that its food is liquidized before it reaches the stomach. Whenever we find a peculiar structure of this kind in an animal we always find, once enough is known about the animal's way of life, that there is a very good reason for it. So far as the lattice-winged bat is concerned we do not yet know why it has developed this liquidizer. It may be that this is the quickest way it can take in sufficient food during the short time it is active each night.

HUMMINGBIRD BATS

There is another kind of bat in the New World which also takes in liquid food but has an entirely different method of doing so. This is the **long-nosed bat** living in the south-west of North America, from Arizona to Guatemala. It not only has a long nose but it also has a long tongue the outer half of which bears bristles, so that it resembles to some extent a bottle-brush. When feeding this bat visits the flowers of the saquaro cactus and also the one known as the shin-dagger cactus. Sometimes it starts at the top of a head of blossom and travels downwards, clinging to it and pushing its head first into one flower and then into another. At other times it may hover in front of a flower for a second or two as it pushes its head into the blossom. In this second case it looks exactly like a hummingbird and in fact what is happening is that the hummingbird feeds on the nectar and pollen of flowers by day and the long-nosed bat feeds on these same substances by night. Both of them not only obtain their food from the flowers but also carry the pollen on their heads from one blossom to another thus pollinating them. It always has been assumed that the long-nosed bats fed on nectar and pollen using their bottlebrush tongue to draw these substances into the mouth. It was, however, not suspected how large a quantity they consumed. It is only in the last few years that a more careful study has been made of these bats by examining them when they return to their roost after a feeding session. Then it was

Long-nosed bat *(Leptonycteris nivalis)*

found that their stomachs were so distended with nectar that the skin of their belly was almost transparent through being stretched. The investigator reported that when he obtained a bat that had returned fatally injured to the roost, he found that the stomach was so distended with the clear nectar that he could read newsprint through the wall of the stomach and the enclosed nectar. It was rather like looking at a newpaper through one of those old-fashioned glass water bottles.

This particular bat had been injured by the spines of the cactus, and the same investigator reported that such injuries are not infrequent. Although the bats visit the flowers, push their heads into the blossoms and even grasp the petals with their toes, they do so with such a light touch that it is impossible to detect any injury to the petals. They use a similar skill in avoiding the cactus spines yet in spite of this they do sometimes impale themselves on the spines, so that they have to tug themselves free and then fly away with what may be a fatal stab.

A BAT THAT CHASES INSECTS ON THE GROUND

There are many other remarkable methods of feeding used by bats in different parts of the world, although the great majority merely catch insects on the wing. From time to time, however, somebody reports having seen one of these insect-eating bats on the ground and there has been a certain amount of speculation, as well as a slight mystery, about what it was doing there. A few years ago a German scientist looked into this and found that the **mouse-eared bat** in early spring has its stomach filled with 50 per cent of flying insects and 50 per cent of insects that live on the ground, such as beetles and caterpillars as well as some spiders. We know that when bats are pursuing winged insects they follow them with the aid of their echo-location. The question arises, however, by what means the bat decides when it overtakes the insect whether it is one it would wish to eat. We have no firm evidence on this point but it is a reasonable assumption that while the bat may pursue its prey by echo-location it must use its sense of smell at the last moment to decide whether to snap the insect up or not. Since the mouse-eared bat is now known to pursue insects on the ground we can be a little more sure on this point. It seems that they can hear an insect moving over the ground provided it is not more than two inches from it, but the insect may be a dung beetle, which the bat eats, or it may a leaf-beetle, which the mouse-eared bat rejects. The assumption is that it uses the sense of smell to discriminate between desirable and undesirable insects, because it has been seen to push its nose into a clump of moss in order to capture a dung beetle, rather in the way that a dog will push its nose into the herbage in order to scent out a rabbit.

HEAVY MEAL, LONG REST

Snakes offer a sharp contrast to shrews. Whereas a shrew must be constantly eating except for short periods for sleep, snakes have specialized in making one meal last a very long time. The original ancestors of the group of animals we now call snakes were lizard-like with the usual four legs, a body and tail, and a head that differed in no substantial detail from the head of a lizard. In course of time the legs

Mouse-eared bat *(Myotis myotis)*

disappeared, the body became very much elongated and the original lizard-like animals became converted into long slender animals that crawled about on their bellies. It is always assumed that this gave the snakes an advantage in enabling them to creep through the grass and undergrowth, but although the changes in the outward appearance were very great they are exceeded by the changes that took place inside the body, and all these are for a single purpose: taking a huge meal and making it last a long time.

There are three main ways by which snakes obtain their food. They may poison their prey, using their fangs, or they may suffocate it by wrapping their body around it and slowly squeezing, or they may swallow their prey alive. There are also such snakes as the egg-eaters. But all, no matter what their method of ob-

Indian cobra *(Naja naja)*

taining their food, swallow it whole, without masticating it.

Since the prey of a snake is usually several times greater in diameter than the snake that will swallow it, obviously the first change necessary was in the jaws. To begin with the two halves of a snake's lower jaw are not joined where they meet in front as in a lizard's jaw, but are held together by a strip of elastic tissue which allows each half of the jaw to move away from the other sideways. At the back of the mouth, where the jaw would normally be hinged or the upper jaw and incapable of sideways movement, there is an arrangement of bones which enables the jaws to make wide sideways movements. Consequently, a snake can open its mouth very wide, and what is more important

this can be increased as the large prey is taken into the mouth. In short, a snake has a tremendously elastic mouth.

All snakes have numerous teeth which curve slightly backwards. The poisonous snakes have two or more teeth that are extra large and constitute the poisonous fangs. None of the teeth is ever used for chewing but as hooks which fasten in the skin of the prey to hold it. Because the separate halves of the jaws can move sideways independently as well as up and down, the teeth form a battery of hooks which are used to draw the prey into the mouth and down the throat. Once the food has been swallowed, which can take up to an hour to accomplish, a bulge can be seen travelling along the body of the snake. Large prey is usually swallowed head-first. A python can swallow a fair-sized deer or antelope, and a grass-snake can dispose of a frog twice the diameter of its own head. Digestion begins as soon as the prey begins to enter the gullet and is continued when the prey has reached the stomach. The gullet is a long tube with very elastic walls and the stomach also is a long tube but it is folded lengthways down the middle so that it is capable of even greater expansion than the gullet. If a snake is swallowing a rather lengthy animal, such as a large frog, the head will have started to be digested before the legs are finally drawn into the snake's mouth.

The food broken down in the stomach is mainly absorbed into the blood stream only when it reaches the small intestine, which is somewhat twisted. The absorbtion into the blood stream may take as long as 50 hours whereas in most animals digestion is completed in two to three hours.

The digestive juices are strong so that the bones of the prey are completely broken down too, although this takes a little longer than the digestion of the flesh, but hair, feathers, bills of birds, claws and egg-shells are usually regurgitated as pellets without being broken down.

Since snakes are cold-blooded, their bodily processes work at a slower rate than those of warmblooded animals. But they have exploited this and taken it much further by swallowing at one sitting a supply of food which can be anything up to 100 times their daily requirement, and they can live by having these enormous feasts at intervals of perhaps a month or longer. Snakes have even been known to live for over a year on a single meal.

MAKING A HEARTY MEAL

The other large member of the dog family, the **wolf,** is as irregular in its feeding and self-centred as the hunting dog is systematic and democratic. The wolf shows something of the qualities of a snake in being able to indulge in an unusually heavy meal and then to be able to go without feeding for an appreciable time. So, instead of bothering with small prey it goes for the larger animals and it may even go without food if these are not available. Having made a heavy meal and become "meat-drunk" a wolf will go a short distance, disappear into cover and sleep for several days. This was noted by the early settlers in North America. A wolf having gorged on a freshly-killed buffalo would be so stupefied by its own gluttony that, so we are told, it could be approached by the hunter and killed by a blow over the head. Indeed, the Plains' Indians are said to have used the over-gorging of wolves in order to destroy them. They would kill a buffalo and cut up the carcase, leaving it overnight for the wolves to over-gorge and then on the following morning they would despatch them.

A few figures will help us to understand this. A wolf weighing 90 lbs., after two days of starvation will eat nearly 18 lbs. of raw meat, so increasing its weight by over 20 per cent. One investigator who kept wolves for study purposes found that 34 of his wolves after a few days of starvation would completely consume in two days all the meat from a horse carcase weighing 1500 lbs.

Wolf *(Canis lupus)*

A BEETLE USES A LIQUIDIZER

We should expect, from their name, that tiger beetles would be predatory and ferocious. No more than an inch or so long, they are fierce hunters, in a miniature way, feeding on other insects. **Tiger beetles** live in dry sandy places, on moorlands, sand dunes and heaths, and there the adults, on their long slender legs, pursue their prey. The larvae, by contrast, live in vertical burrows waiting to snatch passing insects.

The jaws of tiger beetles are strong and as they snap shut provide a powerful means of crushing and shearing the hard cases of their insect victims. They differ, however, from other carnivorous beetles in that their prey is not torn up and devoured rapidly. Instead, a tiger beetle cuts away part of the cuticle, exposing the softer parts of the body. These are then raked into a cavity in front of the

Tiger beetle (*Cicendela hybrida*)

mouth, formed by the bases of the hard mouth parts. Within this cavity tongue-like processes churn up the soft flesh by a rotatory movement, comparable with the mechanical rotatory liquidizer in use in many kitchens today. Any pieces that escape the first mince are re-circulated.

The resulting fluid, with at most very fine particles not liquidized, are then sucked into the mouth and passed on to the stomach. There is, however, not much work for the stomach to do for, while the liquidizing apparatus in front of the mouth is at work, digestive fluids are passed into it from the stomach via the mouth. The food is therefore being liquidized and partially digested in one operation.

TAKING THE STING OUT OF FOOD

When birds drop hard food into water to soften it they are demonstrating that a trick of behaviour can make up for an appropriate built-in piece of apparatus, such as a liquidizer. The **Australian bee-eater,** or rainbow bird, takes us further along this theme. It feeds exclusively on insects caught in flight, and most of these are bees or blood-sucking flies. Having caught a bee in mid-air the bird glides to the dead branch from which it makes its sorties. Holding the bee in its long beak it beats it against the branch, then it rubs the bee's abdomen, where the sting is sited, against the branch until the sting is removed and left adhering to the bark. After this the bird beats the insect's head vigorously against the branch before swallowing it. The whole series of actions is instinctive, so far as we can see, like the rook's method of dealing with cockchafer grubs. This makes the more remarkable the rest of the bee-eater's behaviour. There are flies that look so like bees that people often mistake them for stinging insects. The bee-eater is not deceived, however. When it catches one of these it merely beats its head against the branch.

Australian bee-eater (*Merops ornatus*)

FISHING WITH AN UMBRELLA

Herons are long-legged, long-necked birds with long bills that feed mainly on fish. They will also take other water animals, such as frogs, but they are known primarily as fishermen. There are many different kinds of herons throughout the world and their methods of fishing are, as one might expect, different from one species to another. We think of the heron as standing in water waiting patiently for a fish to swim by and then catching it with a swift thrust of its bill. After this, it throws the fish up and catches it head-first and swallows it, or if the fish is large it may beat it against a rock or a log before swallowing it.

Sometimes, instead of standing still and waiting, the heron will wade into the water and this disturbs the fish, making them swim about, thereby disclosing their whereabouts. Some species of heron rely heavily on these tactics and a few will even execute a pirouette in the water to disturb the fish. More commonly, herons rely on stealth but use other tricks to supplement it. A few species of herons have the trick of raising one wing then shutting it again quickly, and when the sudden shadow of this flicking wing crosses the surface of the water it causes the fish to move and they are as likely as not to swim towards the waiting beak of the heron. Another species of heron holds out one wing while standing with its back to the sun and then puts its head under the wing. This looks very much as if the bird is shading its eyes from the glare of the sun in order the better to see the fish in the water below.

Whatever these tricks may mean, the important point is that in the heron family there are many ways of fishing and in some of them the birds are using their spread wings to catch the fish. The most remarkable of all is, however, the **African black heron**. This uses its wings to form a sort of umbrella. First the wings are spread and then brought forward to form a canopy over the bird's body, then the heron tucks its head under the canopy and starts to feed. The tips of the wing feathers are in the water, sometimes they are actually dug into the mud at the bottom of shallow water. In this extraordinary position the heron waits for a minute or two while the little fishes around discover that here is a shady umbrella under which they can retire into the shade. As soon as they have gathered beneath it, the heron, which has up to this point remained absolutely immobile, starts to strike with its beak and pick up one fish after another.

SUSPICIOUS RATS

There is a persistent story that two **rats** will sometimes combine to carry away an egg. Many people claim to have seen this and with

African black heron (*Melanophoyx ardesiaca*)

slight variations this is how the story goes. One rat clutches the egg with all four feet and rolls over onto its back with it. The other rat, either with its teeth or with its paws, takes hold of the first rat's tail, and drags it and the egg along. Several years ago two zoologists placed an egg on the ground in a corner of a garden where there was a colony of brown rats. They were hoping to persuade the rats to perform this trick. The ground was marked with rat paths where they had continually run backwards and forwards and the egg was placed on one of these paths, after having been carefully washed so that there should be no smell of human fingers on it. The two zoologists then stationed themselves in a hide

House mouse(*Mus musculus*)

Brown rat (*Rattus norvegicus*)

and day after day they watched with a camera ready in the hope of getting a photograph of the two rats combining to carry away an egg. For some days nothing happened. The zoologists lost patience and gave up their task. The following day the egg was gone and nobody saw how it was taken away.

The explanation of this is not that the rats realized that they were no longer being watched. It is merely that rats are highly suspicious of any new object placed in their habitat. Even if that object is food they will pass it by with merely a cursory inspection day after day. Only when it has become familiar to them are they likely to eat it.

HOUSE MICE AS EXPLORERS

The **house mouse** although so much smaller than the brown rat, is very closely related to it, but its outlook on life is very different especially in the matter of taking food. Any new objects put into its habitat will immediately be inspected by the mouse. If these objects are edible the mouse will sample them at once, possibly even carrying them away to make a cache near its nest. This indifference is important in dealing

with a plague of mice, because it means that if poisoned bait is to be used it should be put in as many places as possible rather than at one point or a few places, as with rats. Mice are continually exploring, continually examining new objects here, there and everywhere and will nibble at food wherever they find it.

RABBITS LIKE TO SEE THE NEXT MEAL

With **rabbits** the way in which food is distributed is, if anything, even more important than with rats and mice.

Before the disease known as myxomatosis thinned out the ranks of wild rabbits in Europe, these animals were a scourge to agriculture, taking about one third of the farmers' annual crop. Nevertheless, the bunny rabbit has been a popular favourite in children's books for about a century and in these books we almost invariably see a picture of a rabbit eating a carrot. In making these drawings the artists show that they had anticipated the findings of scientists in the middle of the present century, because when an investigation was made into the feeding habits of wild rabbits a few years ago it was clear that rabbits have a very strong preference for carrots. They will eat these even when there is plenty of other food available. These researches were carried out in order to find the best method of putting poisoned baits to get rid of the rabbits that had not been killed by disease and one singular result emerged

Rabbit(*Oryctolagus cuniculus*)

from this. A rabbit feeds best when it can see more food a little way away. In putting down bait the scientists responsible found that the rabbits took the bait most readily if there was a distance of not more than two yards between each of the baits.

HOW CATERPILLARS CHOOSE THEIR FOOD

Many insects take different food when adult to what they had as larvae. This is especially noticeable in butterflies and moths, so that it is commonplace among those who study them to speak of these insects laying their eggs on a particular food-plant. This is a convenience to those who study insects because it enables them to go straight to the correct plants when they want to find the eggs or larvae of a particular insect.

Researches in the United States a few years ago revealed how the caterpillars of a hawkmoth recognized their food plants, which are tomato and potato foliage. Around the mouth of an insect is a complicated set of mouth-parts, which include an upper and lower lip, an upper pair of jaws, known as the mandibles and a lower pair of jaws, known as the maxillae. On the maxillae of the caterpillar of the **tomato hawkmoth** are some sense-receptors. Caterpillars with these sense-organs amputated ate dandelion as readily as tomato or potato. They also fed on many other plants only distantly related to their food-plant. All the same, they still had "sense" enough to refuse to eat some types of vegetable foods, among them yew.

Tomato hawkmoth caterpillar *(Protoparce sexta)*

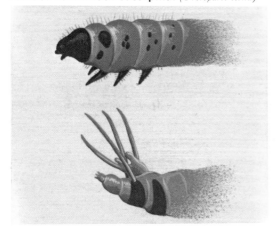

(Above): Front end of larva.
(Below): Left hand jaw, with tuft of sense-organs, seen from below.

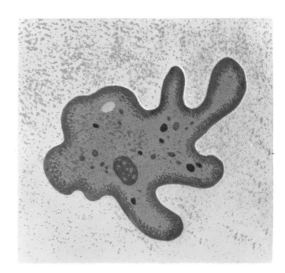

Amoeba*(Hartmanella rhysodes)*

AMOEBA'S RICH DIET

In the second half of the 19th century, when biology began to be a regular subject in the universities, the name of a single-celled animal started to become almost a household word. The animal was **amoeba,** and it was important because it was regarded as so simple an animal that it represented for the student something very near the first animals to appear on the earth. For many decades it was spoken of as a simple blob of protoplasm, but the more it was studied the more it became realized that amoeba is far from simple in its structure.

Even then, we still thought of amoeba as a microscopic animal whose feeding was simple. It is only within the last few years that the chemistry of its food has been studied. Then it was found that a species living in soil, which is very like the amoeba of the text-books, and like it no more than a tiny "blob of protoplasm", could only flourish if a number of substances are present. It needs three kinds of vitamin and seven different kinds of amino-acids, and there must also be a supply of glucose or some similar carbohydrate. If any one of these substances is missing amoeba can survive but cannot flourish.

Instead of thinking of it as a lowly animal that simply takes in any particle of food it comes in contact with, we now have to think of amoeba as a miniature gourmet, very choosey about what it eats and under what conditions it eats it.

HEDGEHOG'S REMARKABLE CAPACITY

The **hedgehog** is a very common animal in Europe. It is so common, even in the outskirts of towns, that thousands of people put down bread-and-milk for it nightly. Nevertheless, although we know that it eats insects, earthworms and snails, as well as a certain amount of wild fruit, we have little precise information on its diet. From the information gained from hedgehogs kept in captivity its appetite seems to be quite remarkable. A German scientist has recorded that a tame hedgehog he kept which weighed 1 ½ lbs, ate one third its weight of meat and milk in one day. Another one in ten days ate just over 4 lbs. of mealworms and during this time its weight almost doubled. However, in the following ten days this same animal ate 3 ¼ lbs. of meat and actually lost 2 ozs. in weight.

Perhaps the ability of a hedgehog to imbibe can be best illustrated by some of its drinking feats that have been observed. One of the best examples comes from a man who found a hedgehog in the garden that appeared to be dying. He made it comfortable on a bed of hay in one of his flower borders. He then filled a small bird bath, a routine he followed regularly each morning. He always put the same amount of water in the bath by filling a pint jug and emptying it into the bath. A few minutes after he had done this on the morning in question the "dying" hedgehog rose from its bed of hay, tottered over to the bird bath and drank until the bath was empty. Since the body of a hedgehog is less than a foot long the animal had taken in at one sitting water equivalent to about one half the volume of its own body. The surprising result was that this apparently dying hedgehog, after drinking such an enormous amount of water, appeared to be fully revived and ran speedily across the grass and disappeared through the hedge.

CAMEL'S WATER LOAD

The most frequent legend about the camel, and the one that dies hardest, is its supposed ability to store water in its stomach, in little pockets in the wall of the stomach. There are many tales of Arabs and other travellers, lost in the desert, being saved from dying of thirst by killing a **camel** and drinking the liquid in its stomach. In recent years all this has been studied scientifically.

A camel may drink as much as twenty-seven

Hedgehog(*Erinaceus europaeus*)

gallons of water in ten minutes but only when it is thirsty, and it can go for longer times without drinking, which means it does not so easily suffer from thirst as most animals. If there is plenty of dew-wetted grass or succulent desert plants it may not drink at all.

Our body is continually losing water and when we go without drink for a long time we become very thirsty, and being thirsty merely means that our body is crying out for that lost water to be replaced. A man can only lose water equal to one-sixth of his body-weight before he dies of thirst. A camel can lose water equal to nearly one-third of its body-weight before it is in distress. Meanwhile its body grows thin, and then when it comes to water it will drink from fifteen to twenty-seven gallons, after which the body is back to normal size or perhaps a trifle bloated. But the water is not held in the stomach, which is far too small to hold such large amounts.

DONKEYS CAN DRINK HEAVILY

There used to be a wild ass in north-west Africa, the Algerian wild ass, but this became extinct in Roman times. Farther east, the **Nubian wild ass** is today found between the Upper Nile, Ethiopia and the Red Sea. It is still there in fair numbers, but it is hunted by the local tribesmen, who eat its flesh whenever they get the opportunity. The only thing that saves the Nubian wild ass is its wariness, so

Camel(*Camelus dromedarius*)

that it is difficult to get near it on the flat plains where it chooses to live. At one time it was hunted on horseback and on camel, but now that the motor-car is becoming common even in those remote parts, and is being used to hunt the ass, it is a matter for doubt whether it will survive very much longer.

It is often said that there are wild asses in the Sahara, but more likely these are the descendants of domesticated asses gone wild. The fact that they can live in the Sahara shows how readily asses can stand up to desert conditions. One reason is that, like the camel, an ass can go for long periods without drinking, and then, when water is plentiful, take a long drink, as much as fifteen gallons of water at a time.

DESERT RAT'S DRY DIET

Kangaroo rats of the desert of the southwestern United States are said to be able to live indefinitely without drinking. No animal can do without water and there are three ways in which it can obtain it: by drinking, by eating food containing a lot of water, or by obtaining what is known as physiological water. Even dry food can be broken down through the chemistry of the body to set oxygen and hydrogen molecules free, these combining to form water.

The kangaroo rat when eating dry seeds is taking food that has as little as two per cent water. What this means can be judged by comparing the dry seed with an apple, which may contain more than eighty per cent water. When eating only dry food, therefore, the kangaroo rat must rely on physiological water, and because its food is dry there will not be much of that. Therefore it must conserve every drop of water in its body, and it does so in the following ways. First of all it does not sweat. Secondly, it does not go above ground during the day when the temperature is high at the surface, but stays in its burrow about six inches down, where the temperature and the humidity are constant. Added to this, its excreta is solid and almost dry, its urine is almost solid, but the most remarkable thing is the way the moisture in its breath is retained in its body. Most animals lose a lot of water in their exhaled breath, and this combined with sweating is why we grow so thirsty in hot weather as compared with cold weather. When a kangaroo rat breathes out, the moisture in the out-going breath is condensed in the cavity of the nostrils, and from there it passes back into the body to be used again.

DESERT ORYX

There seem to be two reasons why animals should choose to live in an inhospitable desert when they could have found an easier living

Nubian wild ass *(Dipodomys deserti)*

elsewhere. The first reason is that they are able to do so because they are fitted by nature to survive on a restricted supply of water. That is, they are adapted to desert conditions. Being so adapted they find in deserts few competitors for food, as compared with the fertile lands. The **Arabian or beatrix oryx,** a medium-sized antelope, almost white over most of the body but with chocolate markings on the legs, used to be common in the deserts of Syria and Iraq. There it has been killed off, but it survived in the Arabian desert where it was secure until motor cars became plentiful in the Middle East. At one time it was regarded as a hallmark of hunting prowess for a man to stalk and kill an oryx, so oryx-hunting became traditional. With the coming of motorised vehicles little skill was required and the oryx became almost a sitting target. But the tradition of going out to kill an oryx remained, and the animal was all but exterminated.

One reason why it should have been accepted as a hallmark of skill was that, in addition to it being difficult to find because it blended so well with its sandy surroundings, the oryx could travel long distances without drinking, forcing

Kangaroo rat *(Dipodomys deserti)*

the hunter to do the same. Whether the Arabian oryx can go entirely without drinking is not known for certain, but one naturalist trailed one for 60 days, keeping watch on it all the time, and he never caught the oryx in the act of drinking. Presumably it got its water largely from the scanty dew-wetted vegetation.

WATER FROM CACTI

There is another kind of oryx living in south-west Africa, known as the **gemsbok.** It inhabits mainly the semi-deserts but it can also live in the vast Kalahari Desert. The gemsbok is somewhat more sturdy than the Arabian oryx but it has the same long curved horns which

Arabian oryx *(Oryx leucoryx)*

Gemsbok *(Oryx gazella)*

the hunters have valued as trophies of the chase. The gemsbok has survived largely because of its ability to live in waterless regions, but in recent years a gemsbok National Park has been set aside to preserve it. The gemsbok obtains much of its moisture from a wild melon growing in the dry surroundings of the desert, as well as from other succulents.

We think of deserts as places without water. It would be more correct to speak of them as places where the water is not readily available. Under the Sahara, for example, are huge underground reservoirs of water which have from time to time been tapped by the peoples of North Africa, as the remains of ancient aqueducts in the Libyan desert show. This is available to such plants as can send their roots down deep. Some desert plants also have the ability to grow quickly during the occasional periods of rain, and some of these can store up water in their tissues, so that they act as water reservoirs for animals. In addition dew forms nightly even in deserts.

The people of ancient times were more aware of this daily supply of water from dew than modern civilisations have been. The amount of dew that forms in a desert tends to be overlooked because as soon as the sun is up it evaporates. There has been, however, within the last two decades a considerable research devoted to studying the formation of dew in deserts, especially by the Israelis in the Negev Desert. They are discovering that the best methods of trapping and using the dew were those used 2000 years or more ago by their forefathers. However, the whole point of this digression is to emphasize that even in a desert there can be available water at certain times of the day, certainly to plants and perhaps also to animals, to a greater extent than we normally suppose. And it is probably true that the gemsbok, and other desert animals like it, profit from dew as much as from succulent desert plants.

DESERT BIRDS

Sand grouse live in dry regions where there is only sand and short grass. They are related to pigeons, and like them drink with the bill all the time in the water instead of lifting the head to let the water run down the throat. During the day sand grouse feed on seeds and any fresh green shoots they can find. They scrape shallow depressions in the ground in which they lie and dust-bathe. They do not seem to mind the heat and this may be because their feathers are set close together, thus insulating the body against the sun's rays and the burning sand. Regularly at dusk and again in the early morning sand grouse fly off in flocks to distant water holes. There they wade in the water and drink their fill before returning from whence they came. It used to be said that sand grouse carried back in their feathers water which they could then give to their nestlings to drink. This we now know is not the case. They do, however, act as water carriers in another way. In the breeding season, while one bird of each pair is incubating, its mate will go to drink. Usually it is the cock that goes to water. In company with others he will fly long distances to a water-hole and on the return journey he brings back a supply of water in his crop for the hen. When the eggs are hatched the nestlings are supplied with water in the same way, the parents disgorging the water from their crops direct into the nestlings' beaks.

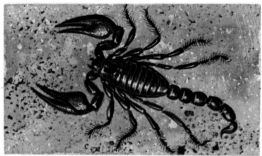

Scorpion *(Scorpionida* sp.*)*

SCORPIONS NEVER DRINK?

Scorpions live in hot sandy places feeding on insects and spiders, usually active at night and resting by day in the sand. They can go for long periods without food, and since to a large extent they get the moisture they need from their food they must also go for a long time without drinking. It has even been said that they never drink, but this is probably incorrect. When scorpions are kept in captivity, in zoos or laboratories, it is usual to put a small pad of cottonwool soaked in water in the cage and the scorpions will visit this daily to lick it. From

Sand grouse *(Syrrhaptes paradoxus)*

this it is fairly safe to assume that when living free in the desert the scorpion probably drinks dew. Equally it is probably safe to say that a scorpion can also survive for long periods of time with no more moisture than is contained in its food.

SWIFT'S QUICK DRINK

Swifts, as we have seen elsewhere in these books, spend the whole of the daylight hours on the wing, hunting insects. We have also seen that the European swift has been proven to roost on the wing. To a large extent it is compelled to do this because its legs and feet are very small and weak and it has some difficulty in becoming airborne once it lands on the ground. Naturally then arises the question how it gets its water for drinking.

We know that swifts use rain for bathing. They may even catch raindrops in the beak when flying, doing so with the same incredible accuracy with which they catch flying insects when flying at nearly a mile a minute. This is something that is very difficult either to prove or disprove. There are, however, times when they come down to take a drink at the surface of a river, but because of their difficulty of becoming airborne again they must do this by a special method. They come down in a shallow glide to a patch of open water and take a sip as the beak touches the surface of the

water, immediately zooming up again. The action is difficult to follow with the eye but there is another action that gives us a clue to what is happening. As the swift rises from the water it makes a shivering action which throws off any drops of water that may have got onto its plumage. This is a built-in safety precaution, a method of ensuring that its feathers do not become waterlogged. A swift bathing as it flies slowly through the rain will also use the same shivering action, and there is a story of someone who had a tame swift that learned to take water from its owner's lips. As soon as it had taken a sip it would fly up and use the shivering action, doing so instinctively, although there was no need for it in this instance.

INGENIOUS TERMITES

Termites, commonly known as white ants, flourish best in areas of luxuriant tropical vegetation, and there the huge mounds, or termitaria, are a conspicuous feature of the landscape. These insects feed mainly on wood, whether it be the dead trunk of a tree or merely the dried stems of smaller plants. There are, however, a number of termites living in deserts, although they do not build the large termitaria seen in the more fertile areas. Nine kinds of termites are found in the Sahara alone and most of these make their nests just under the surface of the ground, in

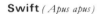

Swift (*Apus apus*)

the form of long galleries or tunnels anything up to 200 yards long. A few go deeper than this down into the ground and in one species, whose tunnels are deep in the soil, all the individuals in the colony are blind. All these termites, whether they are blind or whether they have eyes, seem able to find water. They will tunnel down, as much as 100 feet in some instances, and bring up water in their mouths, to keep their tunnels moist, as well as to use for drinking.

Termites living in fertile regions act as scavengers, clearing up branches and trunks of trees that might otherwise litter the ground. They can also be a very great nuisance to human habitations and works because they are so destructive to anything made of wood or paper. On balance, therefore, termites are something of a nuisance. Even those living in deserts have a nuisance value. Many desert plants throw out leaves and blossom only when the very occasional rains fall. In the intervals between rain, which may be as much as several years, these plants look dry and dead, although

they are capable of springing to life once they are moistened. To the **desert termites** they are as good as dead wood and therefore are a source of food, so the desert termite is instrumental in reducing still further the scanty vegetation in the hot deserts.

Now comes the somewhat surprising feature in this story. There are termites living in parts of the Sahara Desert where there is no vegetation of any kind and for a long time it was something of a mystery how they managed to survive and what they could possibly find to feed upon. It seems now that they feed on what might almost be called fossil wood. That is, on the trunks of trees that flourished where the Sahara now is, long before it became a desert, and are now lying buried under the sand.

UNUSUAL FEEDING TRICKS OF SEA ANEMONES

Sea anemones will catch almost anything they can swallow even animals of large size relative to their own bulk. Their appetites are almost insatiable. By contrast, their powers of fasting

Desert termite *(Isoptera* sp.*)*

are almost limitless and they can survive without food for a very long time. At first, starvation seems to have little effect on them but after a time they begin to diminish in size, growing smaller and smaller, until what had formerly been a large sea anemone is now a very tiny anemone.

The size of a sea anemone is therefore no indication of its age. One that is 70 years old but has undergone a period of starvation, say for a year, may be much smaller than a two year old anemone that has had the advantage of rich food.

Most anemones catch food by waving their tentacles about until one of them comes in contact with a shrimp or a small fish. Then its stinging cells come into play, the prey is paralysed and held, and the tentacles combine to push the prey over to the mouth. It can, however, sometimes happen that a dead animal or piece of flesh may drop direct onto the mouth and then the anemone will swallow this, drawing the food into its mouth by gulping actions without the tentacles playing any part.

An anemone sometimes uses an odd trick to obtain food. It will push out one tentacle until this is as much as six times the normal length, the others more or less remaining normal. The tentacle is then either held motionless until a swimming animal inadvertently touches it and is paralysed, or the extra long tentacle may be used in a searching action to seek out prey among the pebbles on the sea floor. The pushing out of this one tentacle as well as the way in which it is used depends very much on the state of hunger and other circumstances.

There are some kinds of sea anemones that are known as **plumose anemones.** The name was given to them because instead of having rings of fairly large tentacles the upper surface of the body, surrounding the mouth, is decorated with numerous small tentacles arranged in such a way as to suggest plumes of a bird such as an ostrich. For a long time there was much uncertainty about the kind of food they take. In fact, they do not catch their food in the manner of other sea anemones and for the most part they feed on the tiny microscopic animals known as plankton. They will take solid food, such as a piece of dead flesh or the carcase of a small fish if it happens to fall onto or near the mouth, and it seems that they will do this more readily when young than when old. Their main food is, however, the tiny animals in the plankton which are caught by the numerous tiny tentacles and passed on to the mouth by microscopic hairs leading from the bases of the tentacles to the mouth itself.

DAVID ANEMONE VERSUS GOLIATH SHARK

People who live in temperate countries and especially if surrounded, as in the British Isles, with a sea that always seems to be cold, often tend to think of sharks as large fishes inhabiting tropical seas, and sea anemones as pretty little creatures found on rocks and rarely more than an inch or two across.

This, of course, is not so. Sharks when they are young can be of quite a small size and sea anemones, especially those inhabiting tropical seas, can be large. But, nevertheless, the achievement of a Pacific sea anemone in one of the aquaria at Niagara Falls was quite impressive.

The idea of an aquarium at the Niagara Falls must seem odd to anyone who has not visited them. Every day, and especially at weekends, there are thousands of visitors coming to see the Falls. On the Canadian side there are numerous shops selling souvenirs for the benefit of visitors and also several museums and showhouses.

At all events, in an aquarium a big Pacific sea anemone, which may go up to 10 inches across, ate a shark! However, it must be confessed that the shark was a young one, of the kind known as a leopard shark, yet, although rather thin, was thirty inches long, whereas the prey of this anemone rarely exceeds more than an inch and a half in length. So the anemone had to work quite hard for its "outsize" meal. One surprising thing about this incident is that the poison in the anemone's tentacles should have been powerful enough to kill a victim 30 inches long, when normally it has only to cope with prey of at most an inch and a half. If you or I were to put a hand on one of these anemones all we should feel would be a slight burning sensation as its stinging cells poured poison into our skin. Evidently even this is enough to paralyse a baby shark or to kill it.

If a sea anemone had eyes we might say of it as we often do of children "its eyes are bigger than its belly". In other words, this particular

Dahlia anemone (*Tealia felina*)
Plumose anemones (*Metridium senile*)

sea anemone shows us that it lacks a mechanism for telling it how much food it can take.

NEW LIGHT ON AN OLD PROBLEM

People have been eating oysters and mussels from as far back in history as we can trace. Certainly the Ancient Greeks were fond of them and they also noticed that **starfish** ate mussels, oysters and other bivalve shellfish. Today when there are many more people in the world and the oysters and other shellfish are not as numerous as they used to be, ravages to shellfish especially on the oyster beds have become a matter of importance. All the same, it is only within the last few years that the starfish's method of eating the oyster has been understood.

For a long time scientists were divided in their opinions. Some took the view that when a starfish crawled over an oyster it gave out a poison which killed the oyster thus making its shells gape and allowing the starfish to eat the body inside. A more favoured view was that the starfish spread its arms over the shell of the oyster, took hold of the two halves of the shell with the hundreds of sucker-like tube-feet that line the underside of the starfish's arms and by sheer force pulled the shells apart. This gave rise to stories of titanic struggles between oysters and starfish in which the starfish, having a slight superiority in strength, slowly wore down the resistance of the oyster until wearied with the struggle it relaxed its muscles and let the shells slowly open. This seemed a likely story because when a starfish is feeding on an oyster it is humped over the shellfish for several hours on end and then when it walks away all it leaves behind is a pair of empty shells.

Precise studies have now shown that once an oyster or a mussel has closed its shells there is no possibility whatever of poison getting in to kill the animal inside. These same studies also showed that the starfish actually eats the oyster while it is still alive and its heart beating. So poison is not the answer. These studies showed that when a starfish everts its stomach, as it has long been known that it could do, it can insert its stomach through a hole as small as one twenty-fifth of an inch. Tests showed that the starfish could pull open the shells of the shellfish just a tiny bit and through this extremely narrow gap could push its stomach in. Once this is done digestive juices are poured in and the body of the mollusc is slowly liquidized. The wall of the starfish's stomach is lined with cells many of which bear microscopic protoplasmic whips, or flagella, and when these beat in unison they cause a current to flow. As the tissues of the mollusc become liquidized the flagella beat towards the inside of the stomach

Starfish (*Asterias forbesi*)

and the current so produced sucks the liquidized tissues into the starfish's body. These pass through the stomach into the intestine, and after the starfish has been doing this for several hours the whole of the soft body of the shellfish has been reduced to liquid and the shells are left behind sucked clean of every vestige of flesh.

SOUP-FEEDERS:
GLOW-WORM'S SNAIL SOUP

Probably more poems have been written about the **glow-worm** than about any other insect. The famous entomologist Henri Fabre called this beetle a spark fallen from the moon. Wordsworth spoke of it as the earth-born star and other poets, among them Shakespeare, have indulged their fancies. All this is because the female glow-worm needs to attract a mate. She lacks wings but he is able to fly. She lurks in the grass and he must find her. So she carries an illuminated signal. She is able to give out a pale greenish light. The adult glow-worms, both male and female, take no food. The larva is however, carnivorous, its victims being slugs and snails. These it seizes in its jaws and pours out a fluid from its mouth which seeps into the lacerations made by the jaws and slowly digests the tissues of the victim. So the body of the slug or snail becomes slowly liquified and the soup so produced is sucked up by the glow-worm larva.

Glow-worm (*Lampyris noctiluca*)

SOUP-FEEDERS: SPIDER'S CUNNING TRAP

There are certain spiders known as **spitting spiders.** They are found in both temperate and tropical parts of the world. They hunt at night but having fat bodies on long slender legs they move very slowly. Most spitting spiders make no web. Some of the tropical spiders do so, but they are very small webs, not large enough to catch prey. So it was for a long time something of a puzzle how they manage to catch their victims, such as flies, which are fast moving. Nearly 40 years ago a French scientist dissected one of these spiders and found that in the front half of its body, which is larger and more dome-shaped than in most spiders, there are large glands, some containing a gum and some containing a poison. About the same time an Italian scientist had noticed how this was used. He found that the spider slowly approaches its intended victim and, before it can fly away,

Spitting spider (*Scytodes thoracica*)

ejects from its fangs strands of gum which literally pin down and bind the prey hand and foot. The spider than proceeds to its meal and in common with all other spiders it devours its prey not by masticating and swallowing but by ejecting a liquidizing fluid into its body. Its method of eating is, therefore, very similar to that of the starfish and the glow-worm larva and it explains why we see the remains of flies on spiders' webs that have been sucked dry.

SPIDER'S HEAVY TOLL

What we have had to say so far about the feeding methods of **spiders** does not make particularly interesting or savoury reading, but if it appears unpleasant to us there is much to be said on the credit side for spiders as a whole. A British scientist once calculated that on an acre of meadow there is a population of spiders amounting to something like one and a half million. Not all spiders build webs, and some of those that do live in a burrow in the ground and have only a small web at the mouth of the burrow. Others, notably the wolf spiders, spin no web but catch their victims by running at them. So, just because we do not see an acre of ground covered in spiders' webs is no indication that there is not a very big population lurking among the grass and in the ground.

The figure of one and a half million may be

Garden spider (*Araneus diadematus*)

exceeded on certain types of land and on other kinds of soil the number may be less, but it is a sufficiently good index as to the large numbers of spiders living everywhere in the world. So far as Britain is concerned it has been calculated that the total weight of insects destroyed by spiders each year is greater than the total weight of the human population in that country.

FIG SEED EATER

Stilbocoris is a type of **land bug** found commonly in Africa and its staple food is fig seeds. These seeds are also used as a courtship gesture on the part of the male. The male finds and picks up a fig seed which he carries firmly attached to his proboscis. Then he searches actively around until he finds a female land bug of the same species. The seed is shown to her as an inducement to mate and after initially showing disinterest the female will accept it and the male slowly releases the seed from his clasp.

Mating begins only after the seed has been given to the female, and she feeds on it throughout the mating.

The courtship procedure resembles somewhat the type of exchange seen in some predatory insects, the male of which will offer a live insect to the female before attempting to mate with her. We suppose that if he did not divert the female's attention in this way she might eat

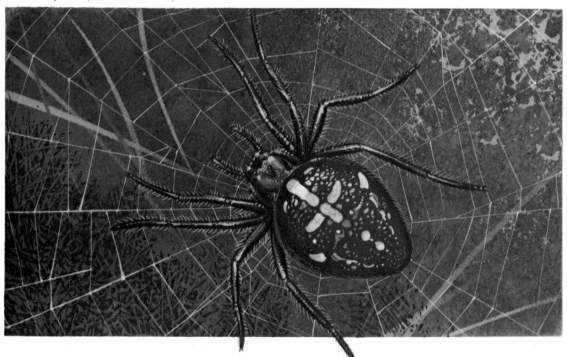

her spouse, as female spiders will often do. *Stilbocoris* is not, as we can see, a predatory insect so that the offering of a mating gift in the form of a seed is rather unusual, and it is hard to see what purpose it can serve. But for this very reason it is probably highly important. Where predatory insects are concerned it is easy to imagine that when the male offers the female this kind of gift it keeps her busy so that she does not attack and kill, or even devour him, when he is pressing his suit. If this is the true explanation then the behaviour of the land bug could mean that the habit arose quite accidentally in the first place, but became stabilized in predatory insects because it proves beneficial to the male, and therefore assists the perpetuation of the species.

Land bug *(Stilbocoris* sp.*)*

WOOL-EATING GRASSHOPPERS

Not long ago a very unusual diet for grasshoppers was reported. A lady on holiday found while picnicing that a **grasshopper** was eating the leather case of her photographic light meter. This struck her as odd because she had always supposed grasshoppers to be strictly vegetarian. It refused to be shaken from the meter and when forcibly removed took the first opportunity of returning to the leather case. She also noticed several of the grass-

hoppers eating her woolly socks, shoe laces, shoes and terylene skirt. As soon as she began to eat her lunch others attacked the paper, some eating holes nearly as big as the top of her little finger nail. Later, she found grasshoppers on her cardigan, eating holes in it, and also her rucksack. At one time she counted 27 on the cardigan, and she realized that what appeared to be grass seeds on the wool of the cardigan were, in fact, grasshopper faeces, and these showed traces of the blue wool of the cardigan — certain proof that they were both chewing and swallowing the wool.

The lady reported that they almost appeared to be drugged; the cardigan could be moved without disturbing them at all. The grasshoppers could be picked up, and then she had great difficulty in persuading them to leave her

Common green grasshopper *(Omocestus viridulus)*

1 Female   2 Male

Red squirrel *(Sciurus vulgaris)*

hand, and had literally to scrape them off. It seemed that those which had been on the woollen garments longest and had eaten the most wool were the most heavily "drugged". The only time they showed signs of quick movement was when, having been removed from the garment, they hurried back to continue their meal. In the attempt to explain this behaviour one suggestion made was that the grasshoppers might have been poisoned by insecticide or weedkiller, and were behaving abnormally as a consequence. Normally they feed only on grasses and a few small herbs. However, as this incident took place at an altitude of 7,000 feet and some way above the line of cultivation, it would be unlikely that the grass should have been treated with insecticides.

As evidence of this remarkable behaviour on the part of the grasshoppers, the lady concerned submitted some of the woolly garments to experts for examination, and they were satisfied that the holes, which looked as if clothes moths had been at work, were, indeed, the work of grasshoppers. Moreover, they had not heard of such a thing before.

RED SQUIRREL EATING DEAD PIGEON AND SQUIRREL EATING SWEETS

By contrast with the wool-eating grasshoppers other strange meals seem commonplace. However, they are worth noting. One can hardly imagine that the dainty little **red squirrel,** who would apparently have plenty to eat in woodland in the way of nuts, seeds, fungi, bark, wild fruits as well as birds-eggs, would want or need to turn temporarily carnivore. This does sometimes happen, however, and there was a typical instance of this observed some years ago in a garden in Pembrokeshire.

A freshly-killed pigeon was left at the foot of a beech tree to be collected by the marksman when he had finished another job. When he returned about 15 minutes later he saw only 4 yards away from him a red squirrel with its head in among the pigeon's feathers. On a closer inspection it was found that the squirrel had eaten quite a large hole around where the bullet had entered the pigeon's breast.

Normally squirrels would not have access to freshly-killed meat, as in this instance, though red squirrels have quite often been known to eat nestlings and small birds. They may eat carrion, although normally this is first attacked by animals and birds for which it constitutes the normal diet. Squirrels will, however, readily take household meat scraps put out for them, but it is certainly unusual to find them eating a freshly-killed carcase.

Other uncharacteristic foods known to have been eaten by a grey squirrel were ice-cream and fudge. A squirrel was seen to pick up a near-empty tub which contained a few drops of melted ice-cream, grasp it between his paws and and drain the tub of its contents, with evident delight. The same wild squirrel so enjoyed a small piece of fudge, that it plucked up enough courage to accept more from a person's hand. If the sweet were wrapped the squirrel would deftly undo the paper and eat the contents. However, in taking the last few sweets he buried the wrapped ones, as he would have done with a nut, at the foot of the nearest tree, and ate the unwrapped ones.

WASPS EATING DEAD SHREW AND BLUEBOTTLE

Those who have lived within several hundred yards of a grassy bank or hedgerow will probably soon enough realize that thousands of wasps live within "smelling-distance" of them. As is known **wasps** can be an incessant

Wasp *(Vespa* sp.)

nuisance in late summer and sometimes within seconds of a sweet-smelling savour being released they are busily wending their way to the source of supply.

Is this a question of hunger or greed? Perhaps it is a bit of both, but maybe the following will make one believe it could be due to hunger. A cat on its nightly prowl had killed a shrew and left it untouched in a conspicuous place. Later the next day swarms of wasps were parading the dead shrew, all eager for a taste of their new find. By late afternoon the wasps had finished their meal and disappeared leaving only the unwanted parts of skin, fur, tail and bones.

Wasps will sometimes show cannibalistic tendencies, but their usual prey are blowflies approximately equalling their own size. A wasp will swoop on a bluebottle, especially one that has settled. It straddles the bluebottle and despite the fly's struggles bites off its wings, then its legs, and carries the body held like a package under its own body and grasped with its legs back to the nest. There the bluebottle is fed to the wasp larvae. This we may call the legitimate hunting on the part of the worker wasps. It explains why wasps still sometimes settle on meat and other carrion, as well as seizing other kinds of insects than bluebottles although these form its usual prey.

The adult worker wasp has no need of body-building protein, because it has already grown to full size at the metamorphosis. It needs only energizing foods, particularly sugar. That is why jam, syrup and honey as well as sweet fruits will always attract the worker wasps. Adult wasps and other adult insects that spend much of their time flying need the energy derived from sugar to replace that used up by the rapid beating of their wings more particularly.

The normal food of the full-grown worker wasp is the nectar from flowers with perhaps a special liking for the nectar of clover. However, the adult workers have been often observed to massage the head and mouth of one of their larvae with its antennae and mandibles, whereupon the larva gives out a drop of clear liquid from its mouth. This substance is in fact saliva from its highly developed salivary glands. Analysis of this shows that it is highly nutritious, containing 9 per cent sugars and considerable quantities of amino-acids.

There is no question of the larva giving this coveted saliva in return for having been fed, for those larvae that do not provide it are fed equally with the others. Using radio-active tracers, it was discovered that only a few "marked" larvae act as sources of the liquid, and these few provide it for the whole community, including the remaining larvae that are incapable of providing it for themselves.

It appears that this liquid, which has ordinary salivary functions so far as the larvae themselves are concerned, serves as a food store which can be shared equally among the whole population. Worker wasps, particularly those whose function is to collect food from outside, starve within a few hours if they are denied access to the saliva. However, they can live on the larval saliva for days without any other food, and to this extent the liquid must act as a safeguard against periods of adverse hunting conditions.

BARBERS OF THE SHALLOW SEAS

A particular angelfish has long been known to the Mexican fishermen, working in the Gulf of California, as El Barbero, because it cleans other fishes. It was not until 1928 that zoologists began to recognize this claim was justified and that other fishes might be doing the same, just as the tick bird feeds by cleaning the hide of the rhinoceros of its parasites, or the Egyptian plover takes leeches from the mouth of a crocodile. In fact, this is now known to be a regular and widespread feature of many marine fishes. In 1949 the American, Conrad Limbaugh, made a close study of **cleaner fishes** while skin-diving off the coast of California. This showed that there is nothing haphazard about it.

Soon after this the fishes were filmed while at work. In the film one could see the cleaner fish at work on a much larger fish belonging to another species, carefully going over its body searching for skin parasites of all kinds. Meanwhile, other members of the species to which the larger fish belonged were waiting their turn in a queue as if in a barber's shop. It showed that marine fishes deliberately seek out and solicit the attention of the cleaner fishes, and that the cleaner fishes themselves take up station at a particular spot to await the arrival of their 'customers'.

Cleaner fishes have been seen to pick off and eat any parasites, including bacteria and fungi, clinging to the surface of the body of their customers, to clean wounds by eating the dead flesh around them, even to enter the gill-chambers and the mouth in their search. Moreover, as the cleaner moves towards one gill-chamber the fish will raise it to let the cleaner in, then lift the gill-cover on the other side of its body when the cleaner moves over to inspect that gill-chamber. · It will also open its mouth to let the cleaner in to search there for parasites. Even a fish that preys on small fishes will allow a cleaner of small size to enter and leave its mouth unharmed.

So a cleaner obtains food and the fish being cleaned is protected from parasites and disease. The barber attracts attention to his shop by means of a multi-coloured pole. A cleaner fish has its station, a particular crevice or other spot on a rock or a coral reef, and this is usually marked by a sea-anemone or a sponge. In addition, many cleaner fishes, especially in the tropics, have conspicuous colours or striking patterns as if using these, like a barber's pole, to draw attention to themselves.

There are other fishes that exploit this situation, to the disadvantage of the 'customers'. They mimic the colours, patterns and habits of cleaner fishes, and when other fishes come to them to be cleaned these mimics fall upon them and devour them.

Cleaning activities, of a similar kind, are performed also by different kinds of shrimp. These have unusually long antennae which are banded in different colours — like a barber's pole. They also take up station in a crevice, often near a sea-anemone, and a fish coming to be cleaned first ranges itself in front of the shrimp to be tickled by its antennae.

Some fishes make relatively long journeys to be 'barbered'. Deep-sea fishes have been seen to come into shallow waters to be cleaned. The large ocean sunfish, with a body like a huge disc, has been seen to wander inshore where a small shoal of cleaner fishes have busied themselves over the surface of its body. Sharks also have been seen attended by groups of cleaners which not only quarter their bodies but enter their gills or even go into their mouths with impunity.

In some species it is only the young fishes that indulge in this practice, the parasites forming, apparently, an infant diet which is replaced by other methods of feeding as the fishes become adult. In many other species, by contrast, this is the main source of food throughout life, and these have narrow or pointed snouts and tweezer-like teeth particularly suitable for picking up small parasites or for extracting them from tiny grooves or crevices in their customer's skin.

THE GENTLE OCTOPUS

Octopuses have the most evil reputation of all marine animals apart from sharks. Any fiction writer can chill our spine with a lurid

CLEANER FISHES

Top: **Longjaw squirrelfish** (*Holocentrus marianas*) being cleaned by **violet-spotted Pederson cleaning shrimp** (*Periclimenes pedersoni*).

Centre: **Smooth trunkfish** (*Lactophrys triqueter*) being cleaned by **bluehead** (*Thalassoma bifasciatum*).

Bottom: **Black angelfish** (*Pomacanthus paru*) being cleaned by **neon goby** (*Elecatinus oceanops*).

story of a diver's encounter with an octopus. Yet for all their appearance of evil, octopuses are not dangerous to man in the sense of making deliberate attacks. Even the big octopuses, that look so fearsome, are normally timid and harmless. If they do occasionally wrap themselves around the limbs or the body of a diver this is accidental. It is the result of their habit of clinging to a solid surface. And when we go into the stories of alleged attacks on human beings we find these attacks add up to very little, despite all the horrific tales that have been written about them.

The truth seems to be that the **common octopus,** which may span up to six feet across the arms, is interested only in catching crabs for its next meal. It will also take lobsters, but crabs are its first preference. Laboratory tests have shown that an octopus relishes crabs above all other food, and they indicate that the smaller octopuses cannot live without them. They will eat fish if there is nothing else for them to eat, but they do this on sufferance, and some octopuses it was found would starve to death rather than touch it. And it is hard enough to kill an octopus by starvation, for in an aquarium a medium-sized octopus has been kept alive for as long as six months without any food at all. This overwhelming taste for crab is underlined by other experiences with octopuses kept in aquaria. When offered both crabs and fish all have immediately seized on the crabs and eaten these first. Some of them have then taken some of the fish but have done so reluctantly, and they have eaten it slowly as if disgusted with what they were being offered. Other octopuses given only fish to eat were found to gain weight very slowly as compared with those fed on nothing but crab, and the young among them soon died when only this fish diet was available.

It seems also that the feeding habits of octopuses are not entirely lost on the crabs themselves. In the English Channel there occur from time to time, at long intervals, plagues of the common octopus. From a breeding ground, perhaps somewhere around the Channel Islands or farther out in the Atlantic, the octopuses spread southwards to the north-western coasts of France, in a plague year, and, having devastated the crab and lobster populations there, migrate across to the south-western coasts of England.

There was such a visitation in 1889 and 1900 when the crab and lobster fisheries on both the French and the English sides of the Channel were completely ruined for the time being, until the plague subsided. While it was on the coastal waters swarmed with octopuses. When the tide was high the fishermen could stand on the jetties and see dozens of octopuses swimming by in the sea. And the crabs, even the large ones, up to seven inches across, came well inshore, seeking refuge in the shallow waters. When the tide went out they could be picked up on the shore itself, as many as a hundred at a time.

One fisherman, working off Plymouth, in 1900, set 180 baited lobster pots. He caught only three live crabs and 15 live lobsters. There were the mangled remains of 44 crabs and 41 lobsters in the pots — and 64 live octopuses. Some idea of the ravages can be gained from the Board of Trade Returns for the summer months of 1900 for the south coasts of England. These showed that the catch of crabs was down by over 280,000 and the catch of lobsters was down by 69,000, representing a drop of 32 and 18 per cent on the previous year. And even that had been a poor season.

One effect of such plagues is that the octopuses must forsake their natural conservatism in the matter of diet and turn to other foods. Having thinned out the ranks of the crabs and the lobsters, and driven the remainder to shelter in the crevices of rocks or onto the beaches they turn to other shellfish, especially oysters.

WHY SQUIDS TURN CANNIBAL

An octopus feeds to a large extent by lying in wait for its prey. Clinging to a rock with its arms or ensconced in a crevice in the rocks, the octopus can see all that is going on around because its eyes are seated high up on the head as if in watch towers. When a crab walks by the octopus launches itself towards the crab with its eight arms all held together out in front of the body. Immediately it arrives over the crab it spreads its arms and drops onto the crab so that it smothers it, preventing its escape.

On the underside of the body of an octopus there is a sort of pouch with a short tube protruding from it. The tube is known as the siphon and the pouch contains the gills. In order to breathe the octopus draws water in through its siphon, the water passes over the gills and is then squirted out again through the siphon. When an octopus swims it uses the

Common octopus *(Octopus vulgaris)*

siphon in the same way but with greater force, in a form of jet propulsion, which drives the octopus backwards. In order to swim with its arms extended forwards, as when it pounces on a crab, it must push the siphon out a little further than usual and turn the opening of the

Short-finned squid *(Illex illecebrosus)*

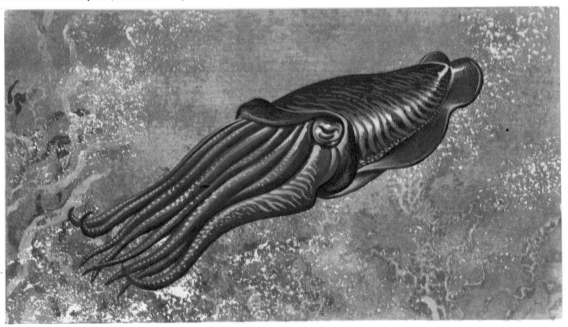

siphon towards its own rear end. If it wants to go to the left it turns the siphon to the right, and vice versa. So an octopus swimming and manoeuvring in the water uses jets of water sent in different directions much as rocket bursts are used for manoeuvring space vehicles. Squids are related to octopuses but have ten arms, eight short arms and two long ones. Their bodies are more torpedo shaped and instead of lying in wait for their prey they move about in schools, often of several hundreds, each squid evenly spaced from its neighbours and all travelling backwards.

Off the coast of North America lives the **short-finned squid.** This is so numerous in the Atlantic waters that sometimes hundreds of tons of them are thrown up on the shores during gales. In addition the squid is caught in vast numbers by fishermen who use it as bait for the cod fishery, and any surplus not needed for this is fed to pigs. Although the squid are commercially so valuable that without them the cod fishery would probably collapse, the fact remains that they also feed on young mackerel, although this is not their normal food.

They usually feed on small shrimps known as euphausians that are in the plankton and they capture these as they are swimming backwards at a fair speed through the water. They do this by slightly fanning their arms so that they create a kind of vortex behind them which draws the shrimps in towards the mouth. The squids can pick them up with their horny beaks and swallow them without checking their speed. That is, the arms are so held that they create a wake that sucks the shrimps in behind them towards their mouths.

Tests have shown that the young squid pay no attention to the small mackerel until they are at least one season old and it seems likely that they have to learn to go for the young mackerel. Moreover, they do so using a different method to the one used for capturing the shrimps. Even a young mackerel is too strong a swimmer to be sucked in by their mouth and the squid instead of swimming backwards as is usual must turn about and dart for the fish in the same way as the octopus darts for the crab. Not only does this result in the squid thinning the ranks of the young mackerel but it also leads to cannibalism because even the small squid are attacked and eaten by the larger ones.

THE BORING OCTOPUS

Crabs are not the only things octopuses eat. They will sometimes take bivalve molluscs, pulling their shells apart in order to eat the soft body. They wrap the arms around each shell, grip with their suckers and then pull in opposite directions. This is much the same as the method used by starfish in opening an oyster or mussel, but the octopus can exert far greater strength. However, in spite of its strength the **octopus** does not always succeed, even after pulling for a long time. It is then that it has to use another method. With its rasp-like tongue it bores a tiny hole in the shell of its prey and through this it injects a paralysing venom. This hole is only about a twentieth of an inch in diameter and much too small for

Californian octopus *(Octopus bimaculoides)*

Ambergris

the octopus to eat the flesh. Therefore, it introduces some of its saliva through the hole and this contains a poison that will incapacitate or even kill the mollusc inside. The surprising thing is that the octopus should go to all this trouble when there must be abundant food around for it to take, because one octopus was seen to spend three hours boring a hole before it was able to claim its victim.

AMBERGRIS

Sperm whales feed on squid and sperm whales give us ambergris. There seems little connection between these two facts, but they may eventually supply an answer to the mystery of ambergris. This is a waxy substance, greyish-white to nearly black that is sometimes found floating on the sea or thrown up on the shore. Every so often, when a sperm whale is being cut up on the flensing deck at a whaling station or on a whaler, a large mass of ambergris is found in its stomach.

Ambergris is a valuable substance because it is used as a base for expensive perfumes. Many people have picked up lumps of wax on the beach and carried them away hopefully, thinking they may have found a piece of the precious ambergris. Most of these hopes have been doomed to disappointment.

Not every sperm whale yields ambergris and it has been said that only sickly whales contain it. It may be present in small pieces or large, the largest lump found weighed nearly half a ton and was valued at several thousands of pounds, and there has been a great deal of speculation why it should be present in the whale's intestine. Associated with the ambergris, often embedded in it, are the parrot-like beaks of **squid**. Moreover, the odour of ambergris derives from a substance known as ambrein, which is found in some kinds of squid. Although it is still a mystery why the ambergris should be there, it seems clear that it is some kind of by-product from the whale's food.

MEALS LITTLE AND OFTEN

The smaller the animal the larger is the surface

Sperm whale (*Physeter catodon*)   **Giant squid** (*Architeuthis longimanus*)

area of its body compared with the volume of that body. An animal is constantly losing heat through the surface of the body. Therefore, the smaller it is the greater its heat loss, because there is proportionately a greater area of surface skin through which heat can be radiated. The animal can replenish the heat in one of two ways: either by taking in heat from the sun by sunbathing or by the movement of its muscles which generate internal heat. The energy for muscular movement, and therefore the energy needed to replace lost heat can only come through the food. Shrews, the smallest of the warm-blooded mammals, are caught in a vicious circle because they must keep on the move to keep warm and therefore must be constantly feeding, yet they must have time to rest. They solve this problem by alternating short periods of feeding and short periods of rest throughout every 24 hours. To feed by day and sleep by night, as other animals do, would be impossible because a shrew without food for two to three hours dies of starvation.

The **water shrew** is even worse off and it is not too much to say, as one writer has put it, that a water shrew is walking a tight rope between life and death throughout its short life-span of 15 months or so, which is the maximum time it can hope to live. Most of them die well before this, however. A water shrew feeds mainly on water insects but it will eat any kind of fish and will sometimes capture small or even large fish and it will readily turn cannibal.

Although able to swim well, a water shrew does not stay long in water. For one thing it is vulnerable to large fish such as trout and pike, and for another it cannot stand long periods of exposure to cold. As soon as it has grabbed some food in the water it comes out onto the bank. It runs through the tunnel it has made in the bank in order to squeeze the water out of its fur, then it combs the fur to get rid of any water that is left using its hind feet, the toes of which are fringed with bristles that act as a comb. If it did not immediately do this the waterlogged fur would cause it to lose heat even more rapidly and it would quickly die of cold. Not only does a water shrew eat its own weight of food in 24 hours, but it does what probably no animal needs to do: it continues to eat while grooming its fur. Most animals have a meal and then groom themselves. A water shrew cannot afford to waste time this way so it combs its hair while having its breakfast.

Although water shrews will turn cannibal they usually only do this when kept in captivity short of food. Provided they have sufficient food several can be kept in a small container and they will not molest each other. The

Water shrew *(Neomys fodiens)*

Rhesus monkey (*Macaca mulatta*)

cannibalism is an indication of their desperate need for a constant supply of food.

MONKEYS ARE COPYCATS

About the time when the researches were being made on rabbits two scientists were studying what **rhesus monkeys** do when confronted with new kinds of food. The monkeys' response was quite different from that of a rabbit, house mouse or rat. When a new food was offered regularly they took only a little at first, although they sampled it in this way as soon as the food was put down. Then, day by day, they took increasing amounts until in the end they accepted it readily and consumed all of it. One noticeable feature of their behaviour was that any monkey being first confronted with a new food and not quite sure what to do about it, would look around to see what other monkeys were doing about it. It would immediately sample it if another monkey did so.

SKIN-DEEP BEAUTY

The **sea hare** has always been something of a puzzle. At various times in the last two thousand years it has been thought to be a fish, a worm, a sea-cucumber, a cuttlefish and a snail. It is, in fact, a mollusc without a shell, and with a squat body and two fleshy 'ears' reminiscent of the ears of a hare, but since the sea hare is never more than a few inches long

the supposed resemblance to a hare is only fanciful.

One feature of the sea hare is that it readily gives out a cloud of purple liquid when disturbed. It has always been supposed that this is a kind of smoke screen such as the octopus and cuttlefish use. But the sea hare obtains greater security from being coloured like the seaweed on which it feeds. When on red seaweed it is reddish, brown when on brown seaweeds and green on green weed. Its colour change is slow, and experiments carried out a few years ago show that the sea hare is coloured according to the food it eats. The pigments in its foods pass into its skin instead of being digested.

Different sea hares tend to select different seaweeds, and recently two American zoologists have tried to find out how a sea hare finds its food. They found that the 'ears' are chemo-receptors, that is, they have a sort of combined taste and smell. They took a sea hare, made an extract from the seaweed it was eating, and anointed the sea hare's ears with it. This made the animal go through the motions of feeding, and by anointing the ears they could make it eat plants it would not normally eat — or even to eat blotting paper!

Sea hare (*Aplysia dactylomela*)

THE RAT'S NATURAL FOOD

There are at least as many rats in the world as there are human beings, which is why we are so painfully aware of their destructiveness. Every year they do millions of pounds worth of damage to standing crops and stored foods. Cereal crops and grain stores are especially vulnerable, but the damage does not stop there. This can be illustrated by an incident that was observed several years ago, when a field of wheat was cut and threshed with a combine harvester. As soon as the last wheat stalks were down brown rats in large numbers were seen leaving the field and making their

living almost entirely on grass seeds. You can see such a rat grasping the stems of tall grasses with its front paws, to pull the heads of grass down to its mouth to nibble the seeds. Cereals, such as wheat, oats, barley and rye are the domesticated forms of wild grasses, so the rat that lives close to men turns quite naturally to cultivated cereal crops, whether growing or in store. In fact, from experiments on rats kept in laboratories it seems that cereals or cereal products are essential to the brown rat's welfare. In towns, where there are few grass seeds and no grain crops, rats get their cereals from bread thrown away.

Some years ago, in the United States, a study

Brown rat *(Rattus norvegicus)*

way towards an adjacent market garden. They stayed for several days in the market garden eating every kind of vegetable they could find, whether green vegetables or root crops. They also sampled anything else lying around. Then, suddenly, all the rats departed. They were reported moving past the nearby village in a ragged column.

This was not because there was nothing left for them to eat in the market garden because there were still plenty of vegetables left. The most likely explanation is that they went because there were no cereal grains for them to nibble. The natural food of the brown rat is grass-seed. Occasionally one may come across a **brown rat** living well away from human habitations and

was made of the rats infesting a number of tenement blocks. First, a survey was made to assess the numbers and also to study their feeding habits. Then the rats were trapped and poisoned in an attempt to exterminate them. In spite of the efforts put into this some of the rats survived and it was not long, once the campaign of extermination was lifted, before the rat population had built up to their former numbers. One reason for this was that as the numbers of the rats fell there was more food per head, simply because the people living in the houses were still throwing away food, including bread. Being so well-fed the surviving rats bred more rapidly. They had larger and more frequent litters and there was a high survival rate among their young.

WILD AND DOMESTICATED RATS

Quite apart from the damage they do people quite literally hate the sight of rats. So strong is our aversion to them that although the most abominable methods are used to kill them, by trap and poison, people seldom raise a voice to protest that this is cruelty. In effect, nothing is too bad, in the opinion of most people, for a rat. In quite remarkable contrast to this attitude is the fact that a strain of the brown rat should have been domesticated and kept as a pet. Yet even this contrast is no greater than the difference between the wild rat and the tame, white or piebald rat.

The wild rat is fierce, aggressive and suspicious, attacking with its chisel-like front teeth on the slightest provocation. When cornered it will fight, fastening its teeth into the lips of a dog many times its own size — if the dog is inexperienced in killing rats. Kept in captivity it will take the first opportunity to escape, and will actively seek for ways of regaining its liberty. Old rats have even been known to get out of traps, and to wait for the chance of doing so. When escape is impossible the rats remain suspicious and tense, so long as they are imprisoned.

Tame rats, the white or parti-coloured rats kept as pets, are gentle and trusting. They make no attempt to bite unless frightened or hurt by bad handling. And they make little attempt to escape. This is partly due to their having been born in captivity, of stock selected for docility. But the main reason for their tameness and for other differences in their behaviour lies in the tame rat having adrenal glands only one-third to one-fifth the size of those of a wild rat.

The adrenals are glands lying on the kidneys that pour hormones into the blood which affect the nerves and increase the blood pressure. When we lose our temper our adrenals have been hard at work pouring adrenaline into our blood, making us go red in the face and put on a fierce expression. In rats, at all events, the adrenal glands have a considerable influence on feeding. For example, when a white or piebald rat is deprived of food its activity increases by only 32 per cent. A wild rat's activity, under the same conditions, increases by 142 per cent.

Left: Two wild rats showing range of colour; right: domesticated white rat.

Brown rat *(Rattus norvegicus)*

WELL FED RATS ARE INQUISITIVE

We can only guess at the reason why the rats, mentioned in the article before last, left the market garden suddenly, while there was still plenty of food. The opinion expressed by an expert on rats was that they departed because their diet lacked cereal. They had been feeding for several months in the wheatfield, mainly if not entirely on grain. Having only green food and root crops to eat in the market garden was probably unsatisfying, so that in a few days they were suffering from something like malnutrition. If this were so, then their adrenal glands would have made them restless, more prone to movement, and approaching desperation, as in the experiments described in the previous article.

All this may have been accentuated by the rich living they had enjoyed during their previous months in the wheatfield. A majority of them must have been young rats, born and grown up while the ears of wheat were forming and the grain ripening. Young rats given a superabundance of food grow more rapidly, are more active, they learn more rapidly, and are more inquisitive, than those reared on an adequate but not over-abundant supply of food. This was discovered when experiments were carried out at Cambridge University a few years ago. One group of young rats were given as much food as they could take in the first week or two of their lives. This group was made up of young rats taken from large litters, a single young rat was taken from each of many litters, their litter-mates being left behind to be suckled by the mothers. Brown rat litters may number anything up to a dozen, and there may be as

many as 21. With so many mouths to be fed the youngsters in a large litter cannot have a superabundance of food, since there is a limit to the amount of milk the mother can produce. The privileged youngsters in the experimental group grew quickly, learned rapidly, were more active and more inquisitive than their brothers and sisters brought up naturally.

Another set of experiments carried out, this time at Cornell University in the United States, may have some bearing on the behaviour of the rats in the market garden. Ten groups of 20 rats were each fed on different diets, so arranged that the number of calories were the same for each rat. All the diets included meat, fruit and vegetables, equivalent to the kind of diet available to the least well-fed third of American citizens. The assumption being, presumably, that this was only just sufficient to keep body and soul together. To this mixture was added ordinary white bread, for one third of the rats, enriched white bread for the second third of the rats, and the last third were given potatoes instead of bread. In spite of the fact that in a wild state rats seek out cereal food wherever possible, a surprising result of this experiment was that the rats with potato added to their diet lived the longest. The experiments were continued for a period of nearly a year and a half and during that time 42 per cent of the rats eating ordinary bread died, whereas only 14 per cent of those with the special enriched

White laboratory rat *(Rattus norvegicus)*

bread died. The big surprise was that $\frac{1}{2}$ per cent only of those that had potatoes added to their diet died.

SHORT-LIVED GLUTTONY

Except when they are being kept short of food for experimental purposes laboratory rats have more food in their cages than they can eat. It is the most convenient way of dealing with them. We have seen that rats given a super-abundance grow more quickly and learn better. Yet any animal over-feeding suffers in health. What then is it that prevents an animal, for example, a laboratory rat, from feeding to the point of getting too fat?

On the underside of the brain is a gland known as the pituitary which is connected to the brain by a very short stalk. In this stalk is a control centre that tells an animal when to stop eating. If the stalk is injured a rat will go on eating long after its hunger is satisfied, and may double its weight in about 8 weeks. Alongside this centre is another, which stimulates a rat to eat. If this is damaged a rat will refuse food and rapidly become emaciated. So these two centres, each made up of a few nerve cells, work something like a thermostat, one switching on to make the rat start feeding, the other switching on to make it stop when it has had enough.

Since the brain and its centres of control, like those in the stalk of the pituitary, are so vital to the welfare of an animal we should expect that there are special measures for their protection. Studies on rats made in Germany showed that these animals can survive from 10 to 14 days without any food at all, although during that time the weight of their bodies went down to half what it was before. With the loss of weight there was degeneration of many of the body tissues, but the cells of the brain remained almost entirely unaffected. This is only as it should be, otherwise, if the centres controlling the appetite became damaged, the rats would either starve to death or feed to bursting-point.

In practice the extremes of death from starvation and super-obesity are rare. Yet, as we learn from the poem, The Pied Piper of Hamelin, there can be lean rats and fat rats as well as grey rats and tawny rats.

There can also be young rats and old rats. But it can be possible for appearances to be deceptive where actual age is concerned. A rat that has been content with a frugal diet, provided it has fed adequately and with the requisite vitamin intake, can at the age of two years look as youthful as a three-month-old rat. And it will live much longer than a rat that consistently gorges itself with food.

Brown rat *(Rattus norvegicus)*

Whether this happens in the wild we do not know. If it does, then to a large extent a proper balance between the two control centres in the pituitary may have had much to do with it. What we do know is that under experimental conditions rats compelled to be temperate in their feeding, by being allowed only an adequate diet with the requisite vitamin content, do not put on weight, remain sleek of coat and youthful in appearance, and live much longer than those given to gluttony.

MOSQUITO LARVA'S MULTI-PURPOSE WHISKERS

The food of the **mosquito larva** is bacteria and minute particles from the breakdown of dead leaves and of the bodies of small aquatic animals. Each larva devours millions of bacteria, and does so without swallowing hundreds of mouthfuls of water. Around its mouth are two small brushes of densely packed bristles. These beat rapidly in a circular scooping motion that sets up a current of water towards the mouth. The bacteria and the particles become trapped in the bristles and are passed back to the mouth, together with some water which is unavoidable. When the gullet is filled with water and food particles its muscular walls contract leaving two small canals open to the exterior. These are lined with tiny combs of bristles. Water is squirted through the canals and out of the mouth, as the walls of the gullet contract, and food particles are trapped by the combs. These are worked up into a ball by further movements of the muscles, and this is swallowed.

It is usual for animal organs to serve more than one purpose. We have only to consider the many uses to which our own hands are put. The feeding apparatus of a mosquito larva

Mosquito larva *(Culex pipiens)*

Land slug *(Limax agrestis)*

similarly serves several purposes. For example, the scooping action of the brushes around the mouth also carries the larva along to its next feeding ground, so that with the same movements it both gorges itself and moves on to the next lot of food. The larva can also feed on the surfaces of submerged objects, and then the currents created by the brushes help to loosen particles from the surface, as well as directing them towards the mouth.

ANTI-LITTER SLUGS

Slugs and snails are pests to the gardener, who needs constantly to be taking measures against them. Yet their true role is that of composters. On ground that is uncultivated they feed on decaying plants. In the first of these they are reducing unwanted vegetable matter to humus, returning the substances in the dead plant tissues to the soil, to be used again by other plants as food. In feeding on small seedlings they are acting as a natural agent for thinning out, and this, as every gardener knows, is essential if healthy plants are to be grown. In both their composting and in thinning out seedlings, these land molluscs play a valuable part in the natural scheme. They become a nuisance on cultivated land largely because weeds have been removed by the gardener and all that is left to them is the planted seedlings. They play another important role in these days when litter is such a widespread nuisance. Because of their taste for any form of vegetable matter they set to work on paper carelessly thrown down and littering the countryside, particularly when this has gum or paste, or any form of flour products on it, as with the gummed flaps of envelopes or the labels on empty match-boxes. Unfortunately the amount of litter thrown down far exceeds the capacity of all the slugs and snails to consume it.

SLUG EATS SLUG— AND EARTHWORMS

There is one kind of slug that should be excluded from the gardener's black-list. This is the **carnivorous slug,** which feeds on earthworms as well as other slugs and snails. We can recognize it especially by its shape. In most slugs the body is broadest in front, tapering behind towards the tail end. In the carnivorous slug the tail end is broadest and the body narrows towards the head. This is in keeping with its feeding habits. Having this narrow head the slug can push it into a worm burrow and seize the occupant. It does this by pushing out its gullet, which is armed with hooks, the gullet being then withdrawn to pull the worm into the slug's mouth.

The carnivorous slug is seldom seen because it lives underground. In dry weather earthworms go deeper into the soil and coil up. The carnivorous slug must follow or starve. It may, in times of drought, descend to 3 feet in the soil and there secrete a cocoon of slime in which it rests until the rain comes again.

WORM'S LABORIOUS MEAL

Gravel is often used to make paths or roadways and we sometimes find on these that the pebbles are heaped in small mounds, each about 3 inches high and 8 inches in diameter, surrounded by an

Carnivorous slug *(Testacella haliotidea)*

area of bare earth 4 inches wide. When we take one of these mounds apart we find at the centre a heap of worm-castings. The mound itself may consist of anything up to 200 pebbles, ranging from the size of a small pea to pebbles an inch and a half across and weighing 1½ ozs.

Darwin first drew attention to this and suggested that they were made by **earthworms.** The best time to see the worms at work is at night when it is raining lightly, using a red light. A bright white light disturbs the worms and they quickly draw back out of sight. Using only a red illumination we see the worm coming out of the centre of the mound and stretching itself to reach the area of bare earth surrounding the mound. With luck we may see a worm moving one of the pebbles using its mouth as a sucker. Standing quietly one may also hear the chink of pebbles being moved,

Earthworm *(Lumbricus terrestris)*

Giant panda (*Ailuropoda melanoleuca*)

just as we can hear the rustle of dead leaves or of pine needles as the worms are drawing these into their burrows. Earthworms draw leaves into their burrows to eat them. They also feed with the hind part of the body anchored in the burrow, the head end stretched out over the surface of the ground and moving like the nozzle of a vacuum cleaner, to skim off the top layer of earth.

A worm that comes up under a gravel path must first clear the ground around its burrow before it can feed. It does this by the simple expedient of lifting the pebbles, one by one, drawing them towards itself while still anchored in its burrow, and dropping them. In time a mound of pebbles accumulates around the mouth of the worm's burrow and at the same time a ring of clear earth around the mound provides the worm with an exposed surface of soil on which it can feed.

GIANT PANDA'S VARIED DIET

The native home of the **giant panda** is the bamboo forests on the mountainous slopes of south-eastern China. When the first live panda reached the London Zoo years ago an appeal was sent out for bamboo shoots. Anyone with bamboo clumps in their gardens were asked to help in supplying the animal with its natural food. Some years later the panda was seen to catch a sparrow that had entered its cage and eat it. At about the same time, Chinese zoologists, visiting the region where the giant panda lives, saw that while its main diet is bamboo shoots and roots it also eats a variety of smaller plants, such as tufted grasses, irises, crocuses and gentians, as well as small rodents, small birds and fishes flipped from the streams with its paw. Some insect food is also taken. In captivity, giant pandas are now fed various vegetables and rolled oats, as well as bamboo, and also receive milk and cod-liver oil. Even with a quick glance it is clear that although the diet provided in zoos is well-balanced it does differ markedly from what the animal would get in the wild. It is equally obvious that this artificial diet is sufficient to keep the animal in good health, but it could well be that there is, nevertheless, something important lacking.

During 1966 considerable publicity was given to the attempt to mate the female panda in the London Zoo with the male panda in the

Moscow Zoo. Mating in the wild takes place in spring; the one or two cubs are born the following January. From all reports the two pandas showed little interest in each other, and the official explanation was that they are too humanized. That is, because each is on its own in a zoo and has only a keeper as companion it almost fails to recognize one of its own kind. This has some truth in it but it may not be the whole explanation, since there are plenty of 'humanized' pets that readily mate in due season. It is known that particular items of diet are necessary, in some species, to bring the animals into breeding condition. It may be the absence of a trace element, that is, a substance present only in molecular proportions, which keeps the animal sterile. Much more research is needed before we can be sure on this point for any particular species, but enough is known already to give grounds for suspicion that the correct diet will offset even humanization.

SILVERFISH

The first insects appeared on the earth over 600 million years ago and we have only a few fragmentary fossils to tell us what these earliest insects looked like. They were wingless and they probably looked something like a very small insect occasionally found in our houses, which is known as the **silverfish,** because of its colour and its shape, although there the comparison ends. We can, therefore, without departing too widely from the truth, say that the silverfish, only one-tenth of an inch long, has come down to us almost unchanged over

Silverfish *(Lepisma saccharina)*

hundreds of millions of years. It is a living fossil.

There are other primitive insects related to the silverfish and they live mainly on small particles of decaying vegetable matter. This explains why we find the silverfish among our bread and flour or behind wallpaper or the bindings of books. They are feeding on flour and paste which is for them a good substitute for the decaying vegetable matter that has formed their natural diet for so long.

Silverfish are sometimes found in the bath or in wash-basins. They have been drawn to these places by the need to obtain moisture for drinking.

HERBIVOROUS LIZARD

The earliest known fossils of reptiles date back

Spiny-tailed agama *(Uromastix acanthurinus)*

300 million years. Already there were numerous insects but the vegetation consisted largely of giant horsetails and tree-ferns. Flowering plants did not put in an appearance until 200 million years later. It is not surprising therefore that the early reptiles fed almost entirely on insects or on the flesh of other animals. Their modern representatives have continued in the same way, because their teeth and their digestive systems have been geared, over a long period of time, to eating insects or flesh. Consequently, very few reptiles, extinct or still living, show tendencies towards vegetarianism. The green turtle sometimes eats seaweeds and some of the iguanas, especially the larger kinds, are almost exclusively herbivorous. The large marine iguanas of the Galapagos islands feed exclusively on seaweeds. Another completely herbivorous lizard is the **spiny-tailed agama,** which feeds on leaves, flowers and fruits. But the young spiny-tailed agamas eat insects. These youngsters have the usual sharp teeth seen in other lizards but as they grow up their two front incisors in the upper jaw drop out and the gap is filled by a down-growth of bone. Later, the two lower incisors fuse, and this blade-like tooth, with the plate of bone in the upper jaw, forms a kind of parrot-beak just inside the mouth, for nipping off pieces of vegetation. At the same time the rear teeth in the mouth become flattened, to give broad grinding surfaces for masticating the plant food.

A similar arrangement is found in the mouths of parrotfishes, which nip small pieces from the surfaces of corals.

HOW HYDRA FEEDS

Hydra is a small freshwater animal a fraction of an inch, related to coral polyps and sea-anemones. Its body is a hollow cylinder with a single opening at the top surrounded by 8 to 10 tentacles. Both the body and the tentacles are capable of being stretched out, and hydra's method of feeding is to extend its tentacles, letting them hang down in the water like so many fishing lines. The tentacles are studded with stinging cells. When a water-flea or some other small animal touches one of the tentacles the stinging cells in contact with it shoot out their threads, piercing the skin and injecting a paralyzing poison.

When this happens the other tentacles come into play. They combine to grasp the prey and

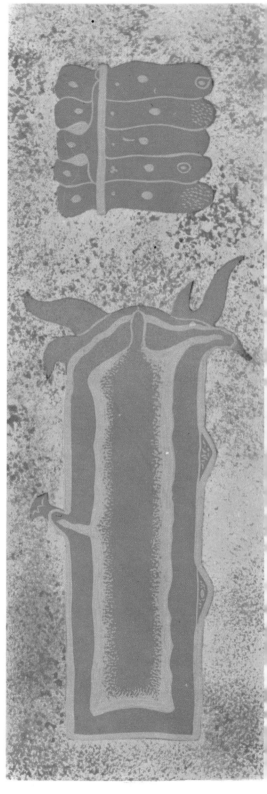

Freshwater hydra (*Hydra viridis*)

82

convey it to the mouth, where they push it through the mouth and into the cavity inside the body. This is a well-organized operation for an animal that has no brain or nerves, only a few scattered nerve-cells. Within the last few years the hydra's secret has been discovered, that a fluid known as glutathione, a substance present in all animal tissues, is responsible. It contains three amino-acids, and the inter-action of these control the movements of the tentacles and cause the mouth to open, once the stinging-cells have struck.

Hydra has long been kept in aquaria, in labo-ratories, for study, but its feeding has been a problem, because it would only take living prey. As soon as it was known about the action of the glutathione this obstacle could be over-come. If tiny pieces of meat were placed on its spread tentacles and, at the same time, some glutathione added to the water, it would accept the dead meat in place of live prey. This deception made possible another discovery. By making the minute fragments of meat radio-active scientists could follow what happened to the food once it was inside the animal's body. It has always been supposed that the cavity in the hydra's body acted as its stomach. We now know that the food is not digested in it but is absorbed into the body wall. This is made up of two layers of cells. The food is taken into the inner layer and part of its goodness is extracted there. Twenty-four hours later the remaining food passes into the outer layer, where it may take two further days to be digested.

So hydra takes three days to digest its food, which is a great advantage. A fisherman, using a rod and line, may have to wait a long time for a bite. A hydra, using its tentacles as a fishing line, may have to wait even longer for some-thing to bump into them. Therefore, it must be able to swallow a large meal and to make it last a long time.

In fact, so long as there is food to be caught a hydra is almost insatiable. It will engulf and digest an amazing amount, and its body then becomes very much distended. At such times one or more buds appear on the side of the body, grow rapidly and throw out tentacles on their own.

KNEELING TO FEED

The **warthog** is found in most open country in Africa, such as thorn bush, thin forest and grasslands, from Ethiopia to Senegal in the north, and from there southwards to the Orange Free State, in south Africa. Years ago it was much more widespread and more numerous, especially in South Africa, where it has suffered heavily from human hunters. Things are even

Warthog *(Phacochoerus aethiopicus)*

Domestic sheep *(Ovis* sp.)*

worse for it today because it is hunted with jeeps, against which its speed of 30 m.p.h. maximum and also its normal methods of defence are of little use. Its usual methods of feeding, moreover, do not help it.

This is an animal altogether unusual, one that has been described as the most grotesque in the world, because of its large and clumsily-built head. Otherwise, the warthog is a fairly normal member of the pig family. It is about 5 ft. long, with its tail adding another 18 ins., and up to 28 ins. at the shoulder. Its skin is slate or clay-coloured with sparse bristles on the body and a conspicuous mane of long bristles running from the head down the mid-line of the back. Its most striking feature is, however,

Ibex *(Capra ibex)*

its very long head, armed with tusks and decorated with two pairs of large warts, with the small eyes set well back and just in front of the ears.

The legs of the warthog are sometimes described as stumpy but they are, in fact, long and with the long head make the animal, when seen side-view and standing on all four legs, look like a caricature of a horse, except that the neck is so very short. This resemblance to a horse is enhanced when the mane is long and falls down over the neck. The reason why the warthog's legs are so often described as stumpy is probably that its characteristic method of feeding is to kneel with the front legs.

It seems to be a general principle in grazing animals that as the legs become more elongated the neck becomes longer, in proportion, so that the muzzle when lowered reaches the ground easily, for cropping grass. The main food of the warthog is grass, although it also eats berries and roots for bulbs, and it seems that in spite of its long head its neck is too short for comfortable grazing, which may be why the animal kneels when feeding.

Herbivores generally are the mainstay of large carnivores. Therefore they have a need for always being on the alert, to make a quick get-away. In addition, the majority of large herbivores, the numerous antelopes, deer and cattle, are ruminants. That is, they chew the cud, which means they can crop grass or other herbage in the open, in a minimum time, then retire to cover, where the chance of surprise attack is lessened, to masticate their food at leisure.

If it is the heavy head of the warthog that has led to the animal kneeling to feed, it is the absence of natural enemies that has helped it to survive in spite of this habit. The warthog's natural strength and enormous tusks make it a formidable opponent, so when disturbed to the point of making for cover it does so mainly at a leisurely trot. This has, however, made it vulnerable to firearms, and to hunters travelling in motorized vehicles.

So widespread and familiar is the habit of large herbivores, of standing on all fours to feed, that it comes as a surprise to see any of them doing otherwise. Yet the **domestic sheep** will sometimes kneel to feed, and so will a goat. The habit is more often seen in the wild **ibex,** which is a kind of goat. All three are by nature dwellers in the mountains, on inaccessible ledges often flanked by precipices.

There, they also enjoy a freedom from attack, but for a different reason to the warthog. It is the nature of the terrain that keeps them secure from carnivores. Their kneeling to feed seems, however, to be more related to their habitat. On step-like rocky ledges, a wild goat or wild sheep may have to kneel on one ledge, while standing with the hind-legs on a lower ledge, in order to crane forward for sparse tufts of grass.

The kneeling may not be habitual in other herbivores but it offers no great difficulty when the need arises, and it is by no means unknown for some antelopes to use this when drinking. Usually, at a water-hole, the antelopes can wade in and drink. Where the margin of the waterhole is several inches higher than the waterlevel, so that the bank drops steeply down, then an antelope will kneel to bring its muzzle to the water. It is the choice of two evils, and it is better to kneel, even if this lessens the chance of a quick get-away in the event of attack, than to have to step down into a pool, into a position of greater vulnerability.

DOG DOESN'T EAT DOG

Cannibalism means eating flesh of one's own kind. Although it has been widely practised in the past by human beings it is regarded by modern society as bloodthirsty, cruel and murderous. Indeed, the very word itself has a most unpleasant ring. Cannibalism is often indulged in by animals, but from different motives, and if we find this slightly abhorrent it is only because we have failed to look at it in correct perspective. In fact, relatively to the numbers of individuals involved cannibalism must be very rare among animals.

Most of the records we have of it are from animals in captivity. For example, when two shrews are placed in a box to be carried home for further study one may kill and eat the other on the journey. This may be interpreted as the result of hunger because two shrews kept in the same box will live harmoniously together for months, provided they have an ample supply of food. There are examples, also, of female animals giving birth soon after capture and eating their young. All such examples are due to stress of unusual circumstances rather than a deliberate eating of a fellow being.

There is cannibalism of a more definite kind

among fishes that prey upon smaller fishes. It may even happen that these may sometimes consume not only smaller individuals of their own species but even their own offspring. As a rule this does not happen because the fry or the young fishes occupy a different niche in the habitat to that inhabited by the adults. Spawning migrations help in this. The journeys take the adults to a place where they lay their eggs and depart. The marlin is an extreme example, and therefore a particularly good one to illustrate this point. The adult lives in the open ocean, one of the swiftest of fishes, preying on squid and cuttlefish and, more especially, other fishes. The latter range from sardines to mackerel.

For a long time it was a mystery how and where marlin breed. This has been partially solved in the last few years by the accidental discovery of young marlin in brackish lagoons situated near the Atlantic seaboard of North America. There is much yet to be learned about the early stages in the life-history of these fishes, but it seems likely that the young marlins do not take to the open seas until they are large enough not to be preyed upon by the adults.

Not all fish-eating species of fishes have this wide separation between their spawning grounds and the normal habitat of the adults, but as a rule there is sufficient to prevent anything but accidental cannibalism.

There is reason to believe that sometimes frogs may eat tiny frogs, and that newts may sometimes eat larval newts. However, no critical research has been done on this, and more often than not this form of cannibalism has been observed in an aquarium or a vivarium, in conditions of captivity that were wholly abnormal. There was the occasion, for example, when someone wished to photograph a row of frogs from one to five years old, merely to show how they progressed in size with age. In the end the photographer had to be content with a picture of a row of frogs ranging from two to five years. Every time a yearling frog was placed at the end of the row one of the others ate it before the photograph could be taken.

No doubt similar events occur under natural conditions, but how often they occur is bound to be very much in doubt. A female frog may lay one to two thousand eggs a year and of the tadpoles hatching from these two at most will survive to full maturity. The rest will die, early or late, from starvation or accident, from disease or from parasites, or from being eaten by predatory insects, lizards, toads, snakes, birds, rats and many other enemies. A few may be eaten by frogs, but it is hard to imagine there is any systematic pursuit of small frogs by large frogs, so any cannibalism will be accidental. Frogs sometimes eat medium-sized frogs, snakes may eat other snakes almost as large as themselves. Usually the eaten belong to a different species from that to which the eater belongs. In any event, when such an event is witnessed, it is often overdramatised, usually by somebody taking a photograph of the victim being swallowed. This leads to over-emphasis and a distorted impression of the true state of affairs.

More often we find there is a natural safeguard against cannibalism. **Lacewing flies,** for example, feed rapaciously on other insects. They will devour, and this is especially true of the larvae, any insect they meet which they can overpower. If we keep lacewing larvae in a box or other restricted space they will eat each other. But in nature the larvae quickly disperse after hatching and it must be seldom that two lacewing larvae meet under natural conditions.

Lacewing fly eggs (*Chrysopa* sp.)

Moreover, there is a neat device for preventing such accidents at the moment of hatching. The female lays her eggs in groups, but each egg is at the end of a stalk, a group of eggs looking like so many pins in a pincushion. Presumably this prevents encounters between the newly-hatched larvae during the first few moments of emergence, when a larva is somewhat slow in movement and could fall an easy prey to a brother or sister that had hatched earlier. As it is, each must descend the stalk of the egg before it becomes exposed to such danger. By the time it is active enough to do this it is also active enough to move away quickly.

It is easier to watch what happens when a clutch of eggs of the garden spider hatches. The spiderlings remain together for a short while, during which time they do not feed. Then, after a day or two they begin to disperse, and only after they have separated do they start to spin webs and then to feed. The young of the praying mantis, probably the most rapacious of all animals (see p. 24), hatch from a cocoon in a clinging mass before dispersing. There is no evidence to show that they start to feed before dispersing or that there is any cannibalism.

Were it not for the oft-repeated remark about the female spider eating the male after they have mated, it would be tempting to say that cannibalism among animals is exceptional, due more to accident or force of artificial circumstances than to a regular feature of behaviour. Even the alleged cannibalism of the female spider seems to have been overdone. To start with, it does not happen in all species of spiders. Even for those species in which it has been observed it may not be the rule. For example, unless somebody has made a special study of this one species and has seen that on each occasion the female has eaten the male, then it cannot be taken as an invariable rule. Perhaps the truth lies in the findings of a German scientist in 1933, on the spider *Argiope lobata*. When this spider mates the female throws a few strands of silk around the male, from which he needs to struggle free, and may lose a leg or two in the process. He may then seek out another female and mate a second time. During this second mating, or immediately afterwards, he dies a natural death.

It is well known that male spiders are shorter-lived than the female, and it may be that the alleged cannibalism of the female has a less sinister side to it than we are usually led to believe. If mating, whether on the second occasion or the first, is followed by the natural death of the male, then the female will be left with the body of her mate entangled in her web. The most economical method of disposing of it would be to eat it. Further, looking at this dispassionately, we can say that it is more a matter of protein conservation than of a sinister cannibalism.

The female praying mantis is also notorious for eating her mate. Perhaps one day we may find similar extenuating circumstances to those just given for *Argiope lobata*.

OSPREY'S DILEMMA

In Volume **Birds, Fish and Amphibians,** on page 18, the story is told of an **osprey** that stooped on a large fish, was nearly dragged down into the water, and only with difficulty managed to reach the shore still bearing this over-sized fish. It struggled ashore with its burden and after a few ineffectual efforts to take off with its load, the osprey was reported to have eaten half the fish, thus reducing the load it had to carry, and so was able to fly off with the remainder.

The moment one stops and thinks about this story it is realised that, in fact, the bird flew away with the same weight of fish, the difference being that it now had half the fish inside it. The question arises therefore whether and in what way it had reduced the burden. As an experiment, the story was tried out on several scientists. The first one to whom the story was told started to laugh before it was finished and when asked why he did this he explained that even if the bird had eaten half the fish the total load it flew off with was in no sense diminished, that there was still the same weight of fish even if half was now inside the bird and the other half in its talons. Most of the others reacted more or less in the same way. There were a few who argued that the load had been lightened, and a small minority of those went so far as to suggest that if you weigh yourself before and after a meal you find little increase in your weight, because the load has been distributed.

It is a common idea that a person, and presumably an animal also, weighs less after a meal than before it. It seems logical, on first principles, to suppose that anybody, or any animal, having eaten a meal would be heavier by the weight of the food taken in. It seems incredible that you can add something to an already existing weight and then find that it weighs less. So the first scientist was asked whether he had any practical experience to justify his laughter. He replied that years ago he used to have a competition each year with a college friend to see who could eat the most Christmas dinner. Each weighed

osprey. After it had dragged the fish ashore it tried to fly away with its load. It failed, and it was only after several unsuccessful attempts that it ate part of the fish. We can conclude that the bird took a little while to consume this half of the fish. During that time its feathers would have dried out to some extent, not only because the water would have dripped from them but because it is a natural reaction of any bird that

Osprey *(Pandion haliaetus)*

himself before and after the meal, and his friend won the series of tests with a maximum increase of weight after the meal of 6 lbs. This is something anyone can test for himself, but it has also been tested in the laboratory with rats and these have shown increases in weight equal to the amount of the food they have eaten. So it seems that the idea that one loses weight after eating is a myth.

There is another aspect to the story about the

gets its feathers wet to fluff the feathers out and shake itself. Moreover, during that time it would have recovered from its exertions in paddling through the water to reach the shore, and it might have experienced some revival of strength also as a result of having taken food. In addition to these minor losses in weight, and the other considerations, we have to remember that that portion of the fish that had now been swallowed was nearer the bird's own centre of gravity, and therefore the bird was better balanced for the act of flying as well as for the push needed for the take-off.

In the course of the discussions that arose after the publication of the story of the osprey it was revealed that one learned professor had witnessed a bushman in the Kalahari Desert eating 58 lbs, of meat in 24 hours, the bushman's original weight being only 116 lbs. It is difficult to imagine that the bushman, could he have been placed on the bathroom scales at the end of those 24 hours, would have been found to have lost weight.

Raccoon (*Procyon lotor*)

HAND-FEEDING THEMSELVES

One of the most familiar pictures in books on natural history, from the simple picture books of our childhood to the sophisticated books of our later years, is of a squirrel holding a nut or other food in its paws to eat it. The pictures may be photographs or they may be artists' drawings. Whichever they may be they are perfectly sound, and yet they are mildly deceptive, because they convey the impression that a squirrel picks up the food with its front paws, using them as hands.

A tree squirrel, such as the red or the **grey squirrel,** has remarkably mobile toes on its front paws. It can use them in a highly skilful manner when climbing. A grey squirrel, for example, can climb along a taut wire, gripping it with its toes, and can perform almost unbelievable manoeuvres on the wire, all the result of a superb sense of balance, split-second accuracy of judgement and the ability to grip with its toes. Yet, when it comes to feeding, a squirrel always picks food up in its mouth, sits up on its haunches and drops the food into its cupped paws to consume it. It never picks the food up with its paws.

Many other rodents, including various species of mice and rats, do exactly the same. When we look into this matter carefully we find, as we pass from one kind of animal to another, that there are remarkably few species other than the Primates that are capable of picking up food with their paws and conveying it to the mouth. The Primates include lemurs, monkeys, apes and man, and these all use the front paws as hands when eating.

Parrots, like squirrels, have very mobile feet, although in their case it is the hind feet. But a parrot can use its feet very like hands, in climbing and in manipulating its food. Tame parrots can even be taught to hold a spoon and to drink from it. Yet, like the squirrel, if you offer a parrot a nut or a grape it will first pick it up with the beak before transferring it to the foot to eat it.

So it is worth while looking at some of the exceptions, outside the Primates. One of the more remarkable is the dwarf mongoose of Africa. This picks up food in the normal manner, with its mouth, but it always drinks

Beaver (*Castor canadensis*)

Monkey *(Cercopithecus* sp.*)*

haunches and crash the egg downwards to the ground.

Beavers will sometimes lift their food to the mouth with the front paws, so will the giant panda. This is true also of the **raccoon,** and it is of interest to note that all three will cradle their babies in their front paws, very much in the manner of a **monkey,** ape or human mother. A few other animals, such as otters, will half-raise food to the mouth, but for the general run of animals, the front paws are used in the manner of a squirrel or are used merely to hold the food down or at best hold it in a favourable position, as a dog will hold a bone, for the mouth to work on it.

by dipping a front paw in water then it lifts its paw to its mouth and licks the water from its paw. Tame dwarf mongooses are very fond of custard, and they will treat this semi-fluid food as they do water, actually lifting it to the mouth with one paw. And it is of interest to note the behaviour of some species of mongoose with an egg. The usual trick is to throw the egg backwards through the hind-legs to crash it against a solid surface. Some mongooses, like the marsh mongoose, will seize the egg between the front paws, sit up on the

Grey squirrel *(Sciurus carolinensis)*

Agouti *(Dasyprocta cristata)*

Perhaps the biggest surprise in this is that it is not always the animal with the most mobile toes that uses the front paws for conveying food to the mouth. The toes of a mongoose are little more mobile than those of a cat or a dog. Nor are those of a beaver. The giant panda, it is true, has an auxiliary pad on the front paws that acts like a thumb, for gripping. At the other extreme, it is not surprising that a raccoon should pick up food with its toes because, outside the Primates, it makes the most skilful use of its toes on both the fore and the hind feet, for holding. In play or in aggression, as well as in climbing and in picking up food, the grasping abilities of a raccoon are very much in evidence. Moreover, it is the only animal so far recorded as having undone knots in string.

The inability to use the paws for lifting is a highly limiting factor in animal behaviour. It is the one thing that keeps them 'backward'. Everybody who knows grey squirrels well is surprised at their resource and skill in stealing food hung out for birds, even in opening containers to steal biscuits. If, in addition, they had the faculty for using their front paws as veritable hands there is no telling the lengths they would go to in their nuisance value.

THE HUNTING INSTINCT

A South African was walking across the veldt accompanied by three dogs. Two were bitches and the third a very fierce cross-breed dog of the lurcher type, known as Vanger (the catcher). The dogs had gone on ahead and were seen suddenly to concentrate at one point, looking down and wagging their tails. They were looking at a young duiker fawn which had been hidden there by its mother and made no attempt to move.

We often say that man is by nature a hunter, or by instinct a hunter. Yet we are told that the human race is descended from tree-dwelling, lemur-like ancestors that fed on fruit and insects. So at what stage did the instinct become born in man to hunt larger game. It is difficult to answer the question because we are still so much in the dark not only about the nature of instinct itself but also how instincts generally come into being. We know even less about how long it takes for an instinct to become established so firmly that it should be such a fundamental part of our nature that it is still there after centuries of civilization.

One theory is that man took to killing large game as the result of living under desert conditions. Experiments with early flint implements suggest they exactly fitted the needs for skinning and dismembering large game. The implications seem to be that under arid, waterless conditions early man was forced to obtain essential fluids for maintaining life from the blood and flesh of these large animals. If so, then he became a hunter by necessity and not by what is normally called instinct.

So far as Vanger and the two bitches are concerned, their forbears were domesticated and selected actually to behave as hunters, yet in this instance, they came across a prey animal but they spared it.

One suggestion could be that there seems to be some urge towards protection of the young, even, apparently, of the young of another kind of animal altogether, as witness the many examples on record of animals acting as foster-parents, even to a youngster of another species. Because of this we are tempted to ask what constitutes a hunting instinct.

A fox cub hand-reared by human foster-parents from the moment its eyes open may not only fail to learn to kill prey but it can be successfully reared on a largely vegetarian diet. Then, we have the well-fed domestic **cat** that will not uncommonly show no interest in catching mice or birds. Linked with this is the way some of the smaller flesh-eaters will treat already dead prey. A tame genet, a small spotted "cat" from Africa, if presented with a dead mouse, will sniff at it, showing acute interest. It will then go away from it, and perform the most amazing evolutions, prancing, bucking, shaking its head and leaping into the air, just as a domestic cat will on smelling catmint. Gradually it draws the dead mouse into these antics, picking it up and throwing it into the air. Only after it has made the inert mouse into an actively-moving object will it attempt to eat it.

From such an example as this it is tempting to suggest that the hunting instinct, as we call it, may spring from the inner urge of hunger, channelled by the sight or smell of prey, but that with some animals it seems to need the sight of moving prey to touch off an excitement leading to a kill. Excitement may therefore be a key emotion, as when a dog merely shows interest in a passive sheep but may savage it when the sheep panics. It may be the same with a fox in a hen-roost that kills more than it needs when the hens rush around furiously.

So we could argue that Vanger and the two bitches were not stimulated to hunting because the duiker fawn made no attempt to move. On the other hand, their failure to molest it could have been the result of a maternal instinct aroused by the sight of a young animal, even in dogs trained to hunt, the presence of the bitches perhaps inhibiting Vanger, the one male of the three. The plain truth is that it is impossible to generalise successfully in these matters.

The same man recorded how, on another occasion, he and his wife were inspecting their kitchen garden, accompanied by four large dogs. A well-grown but not full-grown duiker walked out of the long grass 70 to 80 yards away and stood looking at them. The dogs rushed towards it at top speed and the usual chase was expected. "But the little buck stood still and the dogs walked around it, licked it, and then came back to us."

Not long afterwards this South African was walking through fairly thick bush with a rifle, and with the same dogs. Something produced a scuffle not far away, and when he got near enough to see, he was astonished to find his dogs actually playing with a half-grown duiker, which had tried to run away, but was being prevented by his dogs, patting it with their forepaws, just as a puppy might play with another puppy. But these were full-grown hunting dogs, that had tackled many a wild pig, cheetah, or even, on one occasion, a lion. He called them off and went home.

It is probably an over-simplification to refer to a dog's instinct to hunt, and even more so to refer to man's hunting instinct as though it were an ineradicable urge. We can certainly accept killing from necessity, but more often it is the "excitement of the chase" that supplies the strongest motivation.

A woman living in South Africa has recounted that her father taught her to watch for wild animals but always to end the viewing by throwing a stone or shouting. His advice was "Keep them afraid of humans or someone will kill them". She illustrated the point by describing how the tiny pietje, the smallest buck in her district, used to concentrate in the bush around her house and that of a friend adjoining hers. The buck were not molested. Then, a new ganger arrived to work on the railway and soon boasted that he had no difficulty in shooting the lot.

Was the ganger impelled by a deep-down hunting instinct, or stirred by the excitement of killing something and no more? Why, if "man is a hunter by nature", can so many people readily inhibit the instinct, or even be revulsed by the mere idea of hunting? It seems that the young of all predatory animals require to be taught to hunt, usually by example, and that men originally hunted and still do either from necessity or because of the excitement of the chase, and not necessarily from instinct.

Cat *(Felis catus)*

Printed in Italy.

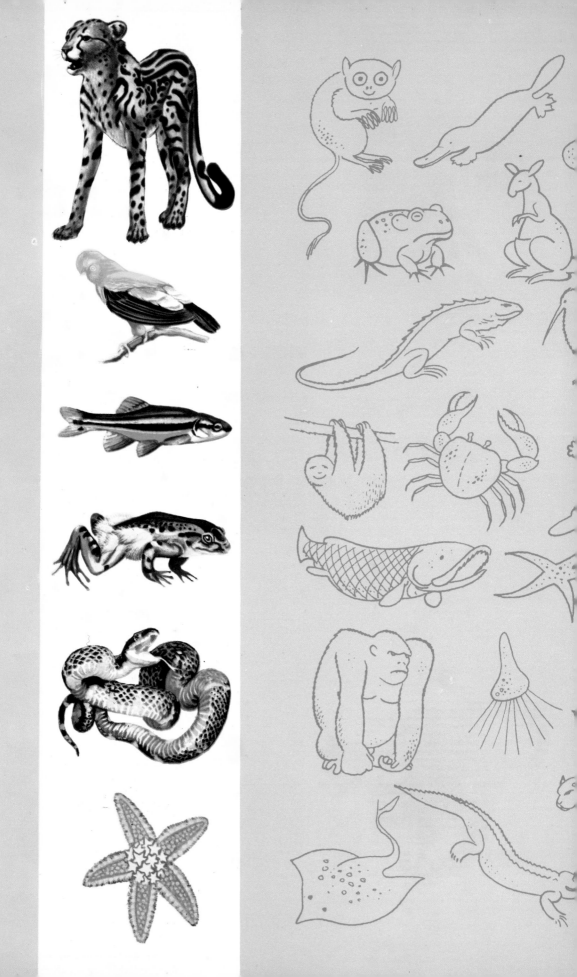